NEW WAYS OF SERVICING BUILDINGS

new ways of SERVICING BUILDINGS

John Bickerdike LIGHTING

J. R. Kell HEATING OF LARGER BUILDINGS

C. C. Handisyde HOUSE HEATING

H. G. Goddard SANITATION, PLUMBING AND HYGIENE

Kenneth Cheesman INTERIOR FINISHES

Philip Scholberg ADDENDA

EDITED BY ERIC DE MARÉ, A.R.I.B.A.

LONDON THE ARCHITECTURAL PRESS

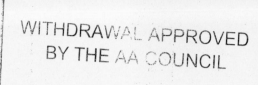
FIRST PUBLISHED 1954

ACKNOWLEDGMENTS

The editor wishes to thank all those who have helped to produce this book. Wherever possible, the architects, designers and manufacturers of buildings, services and servicing plant illustrated are acknowledged in the individual captions. The editor is also grateful for generous assistance, especially in supplying illustration material, to T. Gordon Cullen who drew Figures 1, 2, 3, 4 and 100; to the editors of The Architects' Journal, The Architectural Review, The Journal of the Institution of Heating and Ventilating Engineers, The Journal of the Royal Institute of British Architects *and* Specification; *and to the British Electrical Development Association, the Building Research Station and the Gas Council.*

Printed and bound in Great Britain by Staples Printers Limited, at their Rochester, Kent, establishment

CONTENTS

ILLUSTRATIONS

9

Addenda

EDITOR'S FOREWORD

The success of *New Ways of Building* has encouraged the publishers and editor to produce this companion volume and the same principles have been followed in compiling it. It aims at being a refresher course in the most recent developments and a kind of appendix to the conventional, standard works, which will disseminate information in as digestible a form as possible to busy practising architects, builders, technical students and all others who are concerned with building and its servicing. Unlike the first volume, however, this one may also interest many outside the building industry who are concerned with improving living conditions in their offices, factories, public buildings and homes; even the housewife may find the book of value when deciding how best to light, heat, decorate and generally service her new – or perhaps even her old – home.

Each chapter is written with simplicity and without unnecessary jargon by an expert on whose word the layman, the student or the unspecialized architect or builder can rely. A bibliography has been added to each of the first five chapters to help the reader who wishes to study more. Illustrations have been chosen to be not only informative but, so far as is possible in a book of this kind, aesthetically attractive and stimulating to designers as well.

Lighting comes first advisedly because on this subject knowledge lies further ahead of application than in any other form of servicing, especially on the important aspect of emotional responses. As the author rightly concludes: 'Human needs and feelings are the basic formulative force in design: they thread and link together the material factors. Of all these needs, light has perhaps the widest influence on architecture.'

As will be seen, the newest approach to controlling light is the avoidance of glare and in that the use of louvres and baffles both for natural and artificial lighting is stressed. At the same time, the desire of mind and eye for stimulus as well as ease is not overlooked.

Heating is divided into two chapters – heating of larger buildings and domestic heating, the latter being concerned with hot water supplies and cooking as well as space heating. The first chapter shows the extent to which the growth of theoretical knowledge has improved the heating of buildings in recent years, especially in more control and less fuel waste.

Electricity has a new and valuable part to play in heating; for larger

11

buildings perhaps less as a main fuel than as power for circulating pumps, ventilating fans and forced convection, and in houses for 'topping up', cooking and water heating.

The importance of adequate structural insulation to avoid heat waste and its unfortunate inhibition by high financial cost, are mentioned in both chapters. The relationship between heating and planning, whole house warming and the new types of open fire are well covered in the domestic heating chapter.

Sanitation, Plumbing and Hygiene deals with everything from such fundamental matters (now perhaps of life-and-death concern to the whole human race) as sewage disposal to the design of the latest taps. Pipes and corrosion, prefabricated plumbing and garbage disposal are among the other subjects covered.

The author of *Interior Finishes* deserves a special medal for having unravelled, codified and pre-digested for us, with what must have been research of head-splitting intensity, valuable information on all the infinitely varied finishing materials, natural and synthetic, now available. The section on paints alone should be a blessed aid to all those many harassed people whose catalogue filing is in chaos and whose specification writing is in serious arrear.

The author does not ignore the older materials such as plaster, glass, wood veneer and wallpaper, but indicates how they can be applied in new and interesting ways. He also utters that cry from the heart, so often heard from conscientious architects and interior decorators, for more care by manufacturers in the designing of standard fittings such as door and window handles, and he draws the attention of such responsible bodies as the Council of Industrial Design and the Design and Industries Association to this concern.

The *Addenda* chapter tidies up loose ends such as new ways of electrical wiring, new electrical fittings, fire precautions, partitions. Perhaps the most important section here is that on television aerials, for it may help to mitigate a further degeneration of the sky-line of urban England. In passing, one might ask whether those brutal H-forms are really necessary, even if there is a greater public demand for them than for television sets.

The book as a whole has two general lessons to teach. The first is technical: that structure and servicing of structure must be integrated on the drawing board at the very beginning of a building conception. The second is philosophical and can be summed up in the lines which concluded the Foreword to the first edition of *New Ways of Building*: 'Architects have at their disposal enormous technical scope . . . We live in times of spiritual and financial chaos, unadapted as yet to those stupendous technical advances of the past century which could provide us with the prerequisite of a flourishing culture – physical abundance. To paraphrase a remark by a great modern architect, we have splendid tools in the box; we have yet to make humane, cultural use of them.'

LIGHTING
John Bickerdike

1. PRINCIPLES

Rapid strides forward have been made in lighting during the last few years, and the time when lighting was glibly assessed by the photometer has fortunately almost passed. To-day, lighting is being examined afresh on the basis of a fuller understanding of the way people respond to their environment. Broadly, there are two groups of responses to be considered: the visual and the emotional.

Of the group of visual responses much is known: on eye behaviour, comfort and visual performance, for example; the fairly explicit nature of this knowledge tends to provide the lead to present ideas about design. Of the emotional responses – excitement, gaiety, gloom and the like – very little is certain. But they are, nevertheless, real factors which can and should influence design; it would be a grave error to forget them, even though they are little understood, in favour of the known factors of vision which are only part of the requirements.

Visual Responses

The sensitive surface of the eye, the retina, automatically adjusts itself to the amount of light falling upon it, and this enables the eye to perform usefully over an extremely wide range of brightness conditions – from starlight to sunlight – and to deal with contrasting brightnesses. This mechanism of 'adaptation' is, however, limited in the sense that at any instant only a portion of its range can be useful. Thus, the eyes will adapt themselves to the general (average) brightness of things in view, and will then be able to see clearly over only a limited range of brightness above or below the adaptation 'level'. Those degrees of brightness above the limited range will cause discomfort, and things whose brightness is below it may be difficult or impossible to see.

This explains why, when the eyes are adapted to bright outdoor conditions, we cannot see through to the interiors of buildings; once inside, however, the eyes rapidly adapt themselves to the lower degrees of brightness and things which had seemed dark from the outside now seem well lighted. At the same time we begin to experience discomfort from views through windows of the sky which out-doors caused no discomfort but which now appears too bright because of the adaptation of the eyes to a lower scale of brightness.

This inability of the eyes to adapt themselves to widely contrasting degrees of brightness is at the root of most lighting problems. It causes varying degrees of discomfort and affects our ability to see things – our visual acuity. The effects are termed collectively 'glare'. Two forms of glare are recognized: discomfort glare and disability glare. It is important to distinguish between the two, even though they rarely occur independently, because treatments devised to counteract one do not necessarily counteract the other.

Discomfort

We experience visual discomfort chiefly from very bright sources of light: thus views of bright sky seen through a small window in a dark wall, or of an exposed lamp against a dark ceiling, will be uncomfortable. The degree of discomfort will depend on the brightness of the source *relative* to the brightness of the background; sources which in dark surroundings were uncomfortable may cause no discomfort in bright surroundings. Hence a motor-car headlight causes extreme discomfort at night but none in daylight when the eyes are adapted to a higher level of brightness. Other factors influence the degree of visual comfort.

Source Area. A lamp close to the eyes causes more discomfort than the same lamp in the distance. In other words discomfort is dependent on the area of the bright source. Recent researches have shown that no increase in discomfort will result from an increased area of source provided that it is accompanied by a proportional increase in the brightness of the surroundings: i.e. if fittings are changed for larger ones of the same brightness the surroundings should be made brighter than before to avoid discomfort. It is not enough to maintain only the same source brightness – as is often done in the mistaken belief that discomfort results solely from source brightness. The fact is still unrecognized in many lighting codes where all the emphasis is on the effect of source brightness.

Additive Effects. The effects of glare sources are additive; that is to say, a large number of small sources cause the same degree of discomfort as a small number of larger sources of the *same* brightness and total light output. This allows some freedom in design.

Relationship between Brightness of Source and Brightness of Surroundings. Another factor of major importance in practice is that, if the brightness of the source is increased (not the area as in the previous example), the brightness of the surroundings must be increased by *more* than a proportional extent in order to maintain the same degree of comfort. Consequently, re-lamping an installation with lamps of higher wattage will increase discomfort regardless of the proportional increase of brightness of the surroundings. More light would have to be thrown onto the walls and ceiling or else lighter colours would have to be used in the decoration. In natural lighting the discomfort caused by bright cloud seen through a window is more pronounced than that caused by a blue sky of low brightness – even though the cloudy sky increases the room's illumination in proportion to its own higher brightness.

14

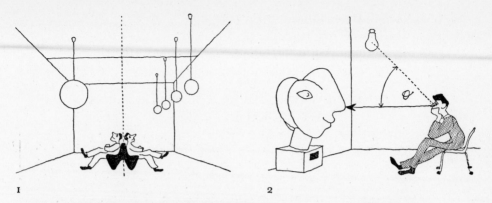

1. *Glare is additive. The effects of small sources add up to equal those of a large source of the same apparent area.* 2. *This diagram shows that glare is reduced when the source is displaced from the direction of viewing. The angle, as shown, should be 50 degrees or more.*

Effect of Very Bright Conditions: In daylight and sunlight, degrees of brightness approach the upper limit to which the eye can adapt itself and progressively more discomfort is felt irrespective of surrounding conditions. Relatively few people can walk about outdoors on a sunny day, when large masses of white cloud are in the sky, without needing to shade the eyes in some way. If this occurs out of doors when our eyes are adapted to the high brightness there, it is not surprising that views of sky cause discomfort when seen from indoors where the brightness is lower. The problem of sky glare is peculiar to this country, as few other parts of the world experience bright sunshine *and* large cloud masses at the same time. With very bright skies large windows cause more discomfort than small ones; to increase the brightness of the surroundings will not reduce discomfort but will increase it. Thus louvres or blinds to reduce sky brightness are valuable. Even a slight reduction of brightness, say with tinted glass, produces markedly more comfortable conditions out of all proportion to the slight loss of light.

Contrast Grading. A sharp jump of brightness from a light source to the area surrounding it causes discomfort, but grading the brightness between the two reduces it. The practical application of this is known as 'contrast grading'. To be effective, local surroundings close to the light source must be appreciably larger than that source. The special value of contrast grading is that it allows the designing of a fitting which sparkles but does not cause visual discomfort. More research is required on this subject before clear practical conclusions can be reached.

Angle of Displacement. A glare source which is uncomfortable when viewed directly is acceptable when removed beyond 50 degrees from the direction of vision (see Table I below). This factor chiefly determines the angle of cut-off required to screen a lamp because, for normal tasks, vision is generally hori-

15

zontal or below eye-level. Industrial fittings rarely have a cut-off greater than 20 degrees, which is clearly inadequate, but there are signs that up to 40 or 50 degrees will be employed in the future.

TABLE I

RELATIONSHIP BETWEEN ANGLE OF DISPLACEMENT
AND DEGREE OF GLARE

Angle of displacement	Assessment of degree of glare
0 degrees	Uncomfortable
15 ,,	Just uncomfortable
30 ,,	Distracting, but not uncomfortable
50 ,,	Just acceptable
Beyond 50 ,,	Acceptable

Shape of Glare Source. Recent studies indicate that a long source mounted horizontally is no more glaring than a square source, but that a long source mounted vertically increases discomfort. Thus, a fluorescent tube set vertically will be more glaring than one set horizontally, and a tall window will be more glaring than a long window of equal area.

Disability

Disability alone arises when there are low levels of illumination where the lighting is from very large sources of low brightness, as, for example, from a large window on a dull day, from a large laylight, or when the source is an indirectly lighted ceiling. The eyes adapt themselves to such large areas of light to the detriment of vision in the darker parts of the room. It would seem that

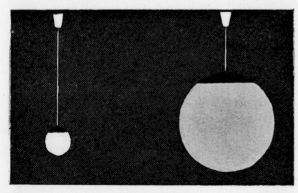

3. *On the left of the diagram is a small source of high brightness; on the right is a large source of low brightness. As the candle power of each is equal, each will cause the same degree of disability glare, but as the larger source has the lower brightness it will cause less discomfort.*

4. *Bright work and dark surroundings (left) lead to reduced visual efficiency. Work should be a little brighter than the surroundings (centre). On no account should the surroundings be brighter than the work (right).*

disability effects are dependent not on the brightness of the source but on its intensity, that is, on the total amount of light reaching the eyes, i.e. area × brightness. It is often impossible to distinguish detail on walls around or between windows. Screening the eyes enables details and colours to be seen quite readily. Disability effects are worst in the area closest to the source.

The Task and its Surroundings. Visual perception of fine detail is at its best when the work or the thing we are looking at is a little brighter than its surroundings. Loss of visual acuity occurs when the brightness of the surrounding area is either very much lower or higher than the point of interest, but the loss is greater when the surrounding area is brighter. Disability is more marked when the task is small. Examples of disability range from the loss of detail and sparkle in a small dark picture – such as a Rembrandt – on a light-coloured brightly-lit wall, to the fatiguing effect of spot-lighting a work point, leaving the surroundings dark; excessive local lighting is, however, more likely to cause discomfort than pronounced disability.

Severe conditions of disability are almost always accompanied by discomfort, or even pain, and it is sometimes not easy to distinguish visual discomfort caused by actual differences of brightness from the mental discomfort or irritation of not being able to see a thing properly.

Attentiveness

One of the most influential of the numerous factors to be borne in mind by lighting designers is that the eye is attracted to light-sources. The term 'phototropism' has been coined recently to describe this reflex action. Phototropism is instinctive: we tend to look at the brightest and most contrasty things in a view, and also at moving things. If these attributes are developed in the things we wish to look at – the work, for example, or some particular object or part of a scene – and discouraged elsewhere, it is then easier to maintain attention. They imply, for example, that the actual workpoints of a machine should be more strongly lighted than the surroundings (this does not conflict with the requirements of visual acuity) and that bright lights or vigorously moving parts on an adjacent machine should be screened from view so that they will not distract attention. Concentration is required to overcome distraction and this when prolonged throughout an entire working day may cause premature tiredness.

Other examples of the importance of focusing visual attention are shop lighting, where it may be desired to direct customers' attention to some particular display; picture galleries, in which the lower areas of the walls where the pictures are hung should generally be brighter than the upper areas; lecture rooms where the speaker should be clearly illuminated and attention should not be distracted by extraneous points of brightness. Theatre or cinema lighting conditions develop highly concentrated attention; motor-car headlights at night produce extreme distraction.

It is clear that uniformity in lighting, as advocated in American 'brightness engineering' is undesirable because it fails to make use of the phototropic mechanism. Even in rooms where no particular focus of attention is desired, lighting the lower part better than the upper will generally make the room seem more comfortable and well-lighted, because our gaze for the most part is directed downward.

Light-sources, that is to say the windows and artificial light fittings, are necessarily the brightest things in view and contrast with their backgrounds; they tend to attract attention and therefore care should always be taken to keep them well out of view and to reduce contrasts around them.

The Relationship between Attention, Comfort and Acuity
Maximum phototropic effect occurs when the area of interest is very bright and the surroundings are very dark; maximum acuity occurs when the surroundings are a little less bright than the point of interest; maximum comfort occurs when the point of interest and its surroundings are of equal brightness.

Clearly, therefore, conditions producing strong visual attraction are not comfortable and do not result in good visual acuity. On the other hand, the conditions producing good acuity are not comfortable in the sense that they require a field of view of uniform brightness which cannot provide a resting place for the eye. However, little conflict need arise in practice. The task can be made the brightest part of the field of vision, and the surroundings lighted well but not so brightly as the task. This provides good acuity, only slight loss of comfort, and sufficient phototropic effect to prevent distraction. With fine work, such as the assembly of small parts, comfort may be as important as good acuity if effort is to be sustained without strain throughout a working day. For coarse work and any job not requiring keen vision but needing constant supervision and individual attention it will be desirable to develop the phototropic effect at the expense of loss of acuity and comfort, particularly when the job itself has little intrinsic interest. Naturally, contrasts should not be too pronounced, and use should be made of *contrast grading* to reduce the sensation of discomfort.

The effect of background brightness is summarized in Table II.

TABLE II

EFFECT OF BACKGROUND TO VISUAL TASK
ON ACUITY, COMFORT AND ATTENTION

Background brightness	Visual acuity	Visual comfort	Phototropic effect
Much darker than task	FAIR	POOR	OPTIMUM
Darker than task	APPROACHING OPTIMUM	OPTIMUM	REDUCED
Equal to task	OPTIMUM	REDUCED	ABSENT
Brighter than task	POOR	POOR	ABSENT

Summary. Each of the visual factors discussed here have a greater or lesser influence on building and lighting design. Certain of them will exert themselves strongly in particular problems. Thus, for example, the effect of the shape of a glare source is of comparatively little significance in most artificial lighting installations as there are few situations in which a vertical source can be efficient and give adequate distribution of light; but in daylighting it may be a critical factor as it affects the design of windows. Similarly, the broad distinction between discomfort and disability effects will often help to clarify problems where the avoidance of one or other is critical. Thus in hospital sick wards it is particularly important that patients should not suffer discomfort; some clarity of seeing could, if necessary, be sacrificed to this end. But for general guidance to designers, the following conclusions emerge clearly from these factors:

(1) The object of attention should be the brightest part of the field of view.

(2) The 'local surround' to the object of attention and the general background should be of progressively lower brightness.

(3) The sources of light should be limited in brightness and area, and should be graded into their surroundings.

Emotional Responses

Emotions range from happiness to sorrow, excitement to depression, calm to irritation; they are affected by work, personality, company and environment. The architect must realize that things seen, heard or felt in building can influence for good or for bad the state of people's minds and emotions . . . the calm and solemnity of a great cathedral, or the gaiety and excitement of a pleasure garden. These reactions are end products and cannot be analysed readily – if at all. But the reactions do occur, though we may never know why, and it should always be possible to associate an effect with its cause.

This section can only emphasize the importance of these reactions. Reactions to brightness and glare discussed so far are more readily investigated, and the future will no doubt produce more substantiating or modifying evidence. They are, however, primary reactions of the visual mechanism; what the mind does with the information it receives is another matter; one of feeling not fact, cf art not science, and ultimately of aesthetics. This is true of the other senses also, and the ultimate refinement of an architect's capabilities will be reached when he is able to create buildings to which people will respond in a manner which he intended. The following remarks are therefore intended solely to indicate the sort of relationship which, we are beginning to realize, exists between illumination and architecture.

Most of the subjective effects of lighting probably come under the general heading of *stimulation*. An environment without sparkle and contrasts in brightness is likely to be depressing: the lack of stimulation induces inattention and sleepiness. Indirect lighting, for example, produces just these reactions because the illumination is wholly diffused and hence without contrast. Perhaps this is appropriate in a sick ward where restful conditions may be wanted; but it is inappropriate in a lecture hall or school classroom where alertness and wakefulness are important. Colour is another influential quality; absence of it coupled with lack of contrast induces less stimulation which in turn reduces alertness. Hence drabness, the visible result of the conditions, is depressing. Experience is showing that the attribute of colour which has the most markedly stimulating influence is chroma. Chroma is the strength or weakness of a colour, that is to say the degree of saturation. Thus, highly saturated hues are more stimulating than weak hues. In the new Hertfordshire schools the knowledge of this has led to the general practice of choosing appropriate colours. Circulation areas, corridors and cloakrooms through which children pass and where loitering is not desirable are usually in strong hues, highly stimulating. Teaching rooms on the other hand have less stimulating colours to avoid distraction. Generally speaking, strong colours are restricted to the chalkboard wall and experiments are in progress with coloured chalkboards; fitments on the chalkboard wall are often brightly coloured. Assembly halls fall in a class between circulation areas and teaching rooms, but here again, to avoid distraction, strong colours are usually restricted to the ceiling and back wall; to focus attention, strongly patterned stage curtains are used together with a dark low-chroma stage backwall to accentuate people on the platform.

In factories, colour and the type of job should be related in a similar way. In sedentary jobs requiring prolonged concentration, use of saturated hues should be restrained, but where the work is largely automatic strong colours might be used with greater freedom to give interest, particularly when people are working at night.

It has been observed that what is commonly understood to be 'gloom' in buildings is not produced by inadequate light but by a particular kind of brightness-contrast: top-lighted museums are notorious for their gloominess; yet generally, in terms of foot-candles, they are better lighted than most buildings. It would seem that gloom results when large areas of high brightness, like a roof-light or window, are surrounded by under-lit dark surfaces; and it is accentuated further by contrasts in the remainder of the room. Highly polished dark panelling can create gloominess solely because any bright sources are easily reflected in it and seen in sharp contrast with its dark colour. The effects are much less marked on matt surfaces (compare, for example, a dry town road with a wet one at night). Thus gloom is caused not so much by lack of light as by disability glare which prevents the eye from seeing into whole areas of detail. If the contrasts are very sharp, we experience discomfort also; it is likely enough that the combination of discomfort and disability lead to an emotional state of irritation. It is reasonable to suppose that easy seeing in the sense of freedom from disability and discomfort will help to foster in a person confidence and zest for whatever he is doing, which naturally leads to a happier frame of mind. These lines of thought are necessarily vague, but the importance of the subject they deal with cannot be ignored. That subject is the *effects* of design on people.

2. NATURAL LIGHT
The Measurement of Daylight
The daylight at a point indoors is measured, in the same way as it is appraised by the eye, as a percentage of the illumination outside. The ratio is termed a Daylight Factor (D.F.). It is often confused with a Sky Factor (S.F.), a similar ratio used to express only direct light from the sky; a Daylight Factor includes all reflected light. A Daylight Factor can be measured in situ, but it is nearly impossible to *predict* it with any accuracy at the present time; a Sky Factor on the other hand can be predicted readily and accurately but can never be measured in practice because it is impossible to exclude the reflected component.

Many rules governing the lighting of buildings are in terms of the Daylight Factor, i.e. the 2 per cent minimum *Daylight Factor* for teaching areas in schools really should refer to a *Sky Factor*.

A 1 per cent Sky Factor is usually the minimum recommended for practice and, depending on the type of building, it is seldom necessary to exceed 10 per cent S.F.

Recommended Sky Factors (minimum):
Factories: Coarse work 2 per cent, medium fine work 5 per cent, fine work 10 per cent or more.
Domestic: Kitchens 2 per cent, living rooms 1 per cent, bedrooms 0.5 per cent.
Offices: 1 to 2 per cent.
Laboratories: 5 per cent.
Drawing Offices: 5 per cent.
Museums: 5–7 per cent.

Three methods of prediction are used. The most popular is the protractor* method devised by the Building Research Station. It particularly appeals to architects because it is a straightforward graphic method, covering a wide range of glazing conditions.

The Graded Daylight Factor (should be 'Sky Factor') Tables produced by the National Physical Laboratory tabulate daylight penetration and spread for all sizes of domestic windows and for obstructed conditions. They are direct in use and much quicker than any other method where large numbers of situations have to be checked – for flats and housing schemes, for example.

The least well-known and most laborious method to use is the Waldram Diagram Method. However, it computes Sky Factors very accurately even with the most complicated external obstructions likely to be found in urban areas.

All three methods are fully described in a paper by W. A. Allen, A.R.I.B.A.†

The Design of Windows
The shape and size of a window affects the distribution of light and the following simple rules give general guidance:
(1) The height of a window chiefly determines the penetration of daylight; width has comparatively little influence. Thus a tall narrow window will

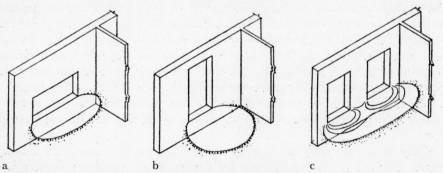

a   b   c
5. *The penetration of daylight according to the heights of windows.*

* Obtainable from H.M.S.O. for horizontal, vertical, 30 and 60 degree glass. 10s. 0d. per set.
† *The Basis of Daylighting Calculations*, by William Allen. (Trans. of the Illuminating Engineering Society, London, Vol. XI, No. 9, Sept. 1946.)

give deeper penetration than a long low one of the same area. (Fig. 5a)
(2) Generally, a high window, area for area, is more efficient not only because it gives good penetration but because it provides a larger daylighted area within a given Sky Factor contour. (Fig. 5b)
(3) The light from several reasonably spaced windows merges to produce a more or less uniform penetration of light. (Fig. 5c)
(4) Penetration of light is curtailed by external overhead obstructions such as window canopies or overhead balconies.
(5) External obstructions, trees or buildings opposite, reduce the light more severely in the depth of the room than close to the window.
(6) Clerestory windows give excellent penetration because they are high, but the area close to the wall is poorly lighted and may not receive any direct light.
(7) A toplight gives between three and four times as much illumination on a horizontal working plane as does a side window of the same area.

These factors are not, of course, the only influences on window design. Views of sky may prevent one from seeing properly and may cause distraction unless the window is suitably detailed. The essentials of good windows are that they should be free from dark and shadowed areas which, when seen adjacent to views of sky, would result in discomfort or disability effects; and, as skies are often so bright as to cause these effects irrespective of contrast, the sky should be well screened from view or its brightness adequately reduced by some means.

Shadowing on windows is minimized by careful attention to the following details:

(a) Shadowed faces should be avoided. This favours slender and internally tapered glazing bars, the inner edge of which should come as near to a 'feather' edge as practical so that all surfaces of the bar receive direct light from the sky. For the same reason the main frame should be splayed and no step should occur between the frame and the wall reveal.

(b) External reveals and heads visible from inside will be seen immediately next to the sky; to reduce contrast they should, therefore, be light in colour as with Georgian windows.

(c) Internal wall surfaces around a window should be light in colour and well lit if possible. This argues for lighting a room from more than one side. Low sills are useful as they allow pools of strong illumination to form on the floor which help to light both the window wall and the depth of the room.

(d) Window bars, frames, reveals and the window wall should be white or a very pale colour.

These features are evident in the traditional Georgian window, which is notably free from discomfort. Georgian rooms generally look well lit even though their illumination levels are often low by modern standards; they are excellent examples of contrast grading. Early designers were sensitive to lighting effects; naturally their reasoning was less explicit than ours to-day but there is little wrong with an aesthetic basis for lighting since by definition good lighting is comfortable and pleasing to the eye.

The exterior walls of modern buildings do not lend themselves so completely to these techniques but modern structure does allow 'window-walls' to be used which need not have troublesome surrounds; the return walls act as effective reveals smoothly grading the change from outdoor to indoor brightness. The pleasantness of a full window is as much due to the absence of shadow areas as to the higher levels of illumination.

The window causing most visual discomfort is one from which there is no view other than of sky – where people are unable to gain relief by looking at trees or buildings. This argues *against* unscreened clerestorys and *for* windows with low sills. The most successful 'view' windows have low heads to cut down views of sky and low sills to help keep the eyes down onto the scene outside.

None of these treatments deals with the problem of excessively bright skies. The discomfort effects are more noticeable with large windows than with smaller ones; this is emphasized by the increased use of venetian blinds and louvering techniques over the last few years. In the past structural massiveness was made use of to screen views of sky, e.g. in the Galerie de Henri II at Fontainebleau the windows are out of sight between the piers. Modern counterparts using structural screening are found in the Boymans Museum at Rotterdam and the roof-lights used in recent schools built by the Hertfordshire County Council (see Figs. 21 and 23 page 51).

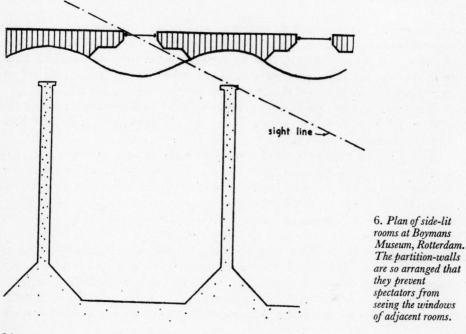

sight line

6. *Plan of side-lit rooms at Boymans Museum, Rotterdam. The partition-walls are so arranged that they prevent spectators from seeing the windows of adjacent rooms.*

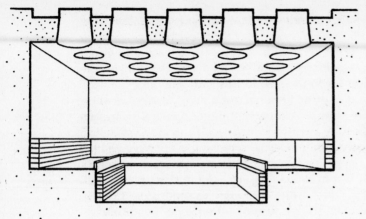

7

8

7. *Cross-section through Alvar Aalto's library at Viipuri showing deep reveals of toplights which reduce sky glare.*
8. *Adjustable vertical louvre blind made of translucent cloth from U.S.A. which can be drawn across the window at will.*

Louvres

The thin modern wall and large window area has encouraged the use of louvres added to, but not forming a structural part of, the fabric of buildings. Venetian blinds, though they do not fully screen the sky, are valuable because they reduce the visible area; and area of source has as critical an effect on comfort as brightness of source. In addition blinds can be adjusted to give full protection against sun glare.

A new type of blind, from America, is shown in Fig. 8. It is an ingenious system of translucent cloth slats which can be drawn across a window; the translucency of the slats is a notable feature, for while it reduces sky brightness, some light can always penetrate into the depth of the room. Other materials like opal perspex would be equally effective.

Fixed louvres will generally be cheaper than adjustable ones. For windows vertical louvres are often best because they do not curtail the penetration of light.

Simple louvering is most efficient and cheap; large slats, few in number and deep in section, screen quite as effectively as small ones, which are more expensive and difficult to maintain. This of course leads back to the more logical solution of making the structure of a building itself do the screening. Louvres should be thin and have a sharp inner edge to avoid shadowed areas which would set up contrasts.

Louvred Roof Lights. Louvres are especially valuable and have a more natural architectural place in roof lights. A simple arrangement using deep crossing screens is shown in Fig. 20. It could be criticized on the grounds that the screens themselves appear to be too bright and that a darker colour for them would help. Thus, if the louvres were, say, three times brighter than the surrounding surfaces, greying them down until their reflection factor became one-third of

25

that of the surrounding colour would eliminate most of the contrast, and viewing conditions would be greatly improved. Louvering of top-lights in existing buildings where sky glare conditions are bad can result in remarkable visual improvements, for example, in factories. In new buildings the use of the structure for screening is the most logical means to this end (Fig. 22).

Sun Louvres. Internal louvres are a protection against glare and local heating effects from the sun, but they are valueless in preventing the general heat-gain in a building, for once the sun's rays have passed through the glass, their full heating effect will be felt internally. Only external screening is effective against heat penetration from the sun. In countries where the sun has to be screened, the *brise-soleil* is perhaps the logical conclusion (Fig. 16), but in this country such extreme measures can never be of full value although examples do exist in which the *brise-soleil* has been adapted to British sun and sky glare conditions.

3. ARTIFICIAL LIGHT

Sources of Light

Terms. The unit of light measurement is the lumen* (L). For example, the output of a 300-watt lamp is specified as 4,400 lumens, that of a 100-watt lamp as 1,100 lumens. The 300-watt lamp is clearly more efficient because it gives nearly 15 lumens for each watt whereas the 100-watt lamp can give only $11\frac{1}{2}$ lumens. The lumen per watt (L/W) is therefore the unit with which the efficiency of lamps is compared. Illumination at a point is measured in lumens per square foot (L/ft²) or Foot-candles.

Three artificial sources of light are in general use to-day: incandescent lamps, gas discharge lamps and fluorescent tubes.

Incandescent Lamps. The incandescent lamp first appeared about 1880. Its efficiency has been steadily raised until to-day the coiled-coil filament lamp probably represents the peak of development in this type as the operating temperature of the tungsten filament is now close to its melting point. Maximum efficiency is 15–18 L/W.

Gas Discharge Lamps. In discharge lamps, light is produced by the passage of electrical energy through certain vapours. Efficiency in use of current is high, three to four times that of filament lamps, but unfortunately the light is not white. Mercury vapour gives bluish-white light and sodium vapour a pronounced chrome-yellow light. In spite of this, both sources are occasionally used in factories because of their high efficiencies, but the results are unsatisfactory.

The colour defect has led to the development of the mercury tungsten lamp which is a discharge tube and a tungsten filament within a common outer bulb.

---

* A lumen is the amount of light falling on one square foot of the surface of a sphere of one foot radius when a 'standard candle' is placed at the centre of the sphere. (Conversely, one candle is equivalent to 12.5 lumens.)

Its efficiency lies between that of mercury and tungsten lamps. Although colour distortion still occurs, the predominance of red in the tungsten light makes up for its deficiency in the discharge. Its use is confined to industrial buildings.

Fluorescent Lamps. (*Hot Cathode Type.*) The fluorescent lamp is a discharge lamp of a special kind, usually in tube form, between one and eight feet long, which is coated internally with a powder which becomes luminous when exposed to the discharge. The colour of the light is wholly determined by the nature of the powder. It can closely simulate daylight and, by using a suitable mixture of powders, a full range of coloured tubes is possible.

Efficiency and Cost. The efficiency of fluorescent lamps is between two and four times that of tungsten filament lamps and they have a much longer life: 2,500 to 5,000 hours compared with about 1,000 hours for tungsten.

Assessment of comparative costs is not straightforward as it depends on hours of operation and cost of electricity. A fluorescent tube is several times dearer than a tungsten lamp but allowing for its higher efficiency and longer life there is probably little to choose in ultimate cost between the two. But fluorescent lighting needs expensive control gear and the fittings are invariably costlier; hence installation costs are higher.

Running costs are calculated on a lumen-hour basis, a convenient forumula being,

$$C = \frac{1,000}{F} \left[\frac{Cl}{L} + (Cc \times P) \right]$$

Where C=total running in pence per million lumen-hours; Cl=cost of lamps in pence; Cc=cost of current in pence per unit; F=lumen output of lamp; L=life of lamp, in thousands of hours; P=wattage of lamp. When calculating Cc, allowance must be made for any kw. or maximum demand charges, divided by the estimated annual burning hours.

Generally, fluorescent lighting is cheaper to run; but as it mixes so well with daylight the saving may be offset by its greater use during daylight hours, or by its being turned on earlier in the evenings when the colour of incandescent light would be unpleasant.

Colour. The three commonest tubes are 'daylight', 'natural' and 'warm-white'. The 'daylight' and 'natural' lamps are close to daylight colour and mix well with it. Both have a slight blue bias. The 'warm-white' employs powders to increase the red content of the light in a not-too-successful attempt to create a pleasanter light. Time is proving the 'natural' tube to be the most popular, but the 'daylight' tube is probably more frequently used because of its slightly higher efficiency.

The colour of tungsten lamps is acceptable in most situations; its spectrum is continuous, that is to say, no colours are missing, but it is biased toward the red end. This means that colours are not greatly displaced relative to each other. The spectrum of a fluorescent lamp is discontinuous, it has certain pronounced spectrum 'lines' which enhance colours coinciding with them and depress others. Fluorescent lighting alone cannot yet be used with complete confidence in places where slight distortion can have unpleasant effects, for example, on food in restaurants.

Stroboscopic Effect. Flicker is caused by the extinguishing of the vapour discharge twice per cycle, i.e. 100 times per second on a normal 50-cycle A.C. supply. Thus, an object rotating at a speed exactly proportional to the cycle frequency will appear to be stationary, or, at other speeds, may appear to be rotating slowly. The effect can be troublesome and may even be dangerous in, for example, machine shops. Several lamps, fairly close together, connected in suitable phase relationships, can largely eliminate the effect; but this tends to exclude the use of single-tube fittings for local lighting over moving machinery. Some tubes (chiefly the common 80 w. 5 ft. type) with bayonet-cap ends should have the first two inches of each end covered to mask 'end-flicker' caused by the extinguishing of the electrodes. End-flicker is more noticeable because its frequency is 50 times per second.*

Cold-Cathode Fluorescent Lamps. Another form of the fluorescent lamp is the cold-cathode tube. The quality of its light is about the same as that of the hot-cathode tube but its efficiency is slightly lower. Its merit is a very long life, 10,000 to 15,000 hours, and instantaneous starting. (Special control gear is now also available for instantaneous starting of hot-cathode tubes.)

The cost of installing tubes and gear, not including fittings, is about equal to the cost of hot-cathode installations including the fittings. Cold-cathode lamps run on a high voltage – 1,200–1,500 volts – which is a potential danger, often limiting their use to situations out of normal reach. Cold-cathode lighting is being used fairly extensively in Australia where single-pin end-cap fixings have been developed for easy re-lamping and to lessen the dangers of the high operating voltage.

High efficiency is obtained only in long lengths, minimum about 8 ft. 6 in., and in batches of three served by one transformer.

The general properties and dimensions of incandescent, discharge and fluorescent lamps are compared in Table III.

Installations

Fluorescent tubes are large and will give only diffuse lighting: incandescent lamps are small and will give clearly defined lighting – sharp shadows and sparkling highlights. Diffuse lighting tends to destroy the form of things and by the lack of sparkle and stimulating contrast can lead to soporific conditions: on the other hand, lighting which is too well-defined may be over-contrasty,

---

* The effects of flicker on vision are at present being studied by the B.R.S., but no results are yet available. Lamp manufacturers are also striving to produce fluorescent powder mixtures with a more sustained 'after-glow' to minimize flicker.

TABLE III PROPERTIES AND DIMENSIONS OF FILAMENT, FLUORESCENT, SODIUM-VAPOUR AND MERCURY-VAPOUR LAMPS

TUNGSTEN FILAMENT

Type	Description	Dimensions				Life	Average lumens per watt throughout life
		A: in.	B: in.	C: in.	D: in.	hrs.	
Tungsten filament	15 W BC or ES	$3\frac{5}{8}$	$2\frac{3}{16}$	$2\frac{1}{2}$	$1\frac{3}{16}$		7.5
	25 W ,, ,, ,,	$2\frac{15}{16}$	$2\frac{3}{8}$	$2\frac{3}{4}$	$1\frac{5}{16}$		8.2
	40 W ,, ,, ,,	$4\frac{5}{16}$	$2\frac{3}{8}$	$3\frac{1}{8}$	$1\frac{5}{16}$		8.2 (10)
	60 W ,, ,, ,,	$4\frac{5}{8}$	$2\frac{9}{16}$	$3\frac{5}{16}$	$1\frac{3}{8}$	1,000 nominal	10.0 (11)
	75 W ,, ,, ,,	$4\frac{7}{8}$	$2\frac{3}{4}$	$3\frac{1}{2}$	$1\frac{1}{2}$		10.0 (12)
Standard bayonet cap (BC)	100 W ,, ,, ,,	$5\frac{3}{8}$	$2\frac{15}{16}$	$3\frac{15}{16}$	$1\frac{1}{2}$		11.6 (13)
	150 W BC or ES	$6\frac{1}{4}$	$3\frac{1}{8}$	$4\frac{3}{4}$	$1\frac{1}{2}$		13.0
	200 W ,, ,, ,,	7	$3\frac{1}{2}$	$5\frac{1}{4}$	$1\frac{1}{4}$		13.5
	300 W ES	$9\frac{1}{4}$	$4\frac{5}{16}$	7	$1\frac{15}{16}$		14.8
	500 W ES	$10\frac{1}{2}$	$5\frac{5}{8}$	$7\frac{15}{16}$	2	1,000 nominal	16.0
	750 W ES	$11\frac{1}{4}$	$5\frac{7}{8}$	$8\frac{7}{8}$	$2\frac{3}{16}$		17.0
	1,000 W ES	$11\frac{3}{8}$	$5\frac{5}{8}$	$8\frac{5}{8}$	$2\frac{3}{16}$		17.8
Edison screw cap (ES) or Goliath ES (GES)	1,500 W ES	$13\frac{1}{4}$	$6\frac{11}{16}$	$9\frac{13}{16}$	$2\frac{3}{8}$		19.0

(coiled coil)

FLUORESCENT, MERCURY-VAPOUR AND SODIUM-VAPOUR

Type	Description	Dimensions		Life	Average lumens per watt throughout life*		
		A: ft.	B: in.	hrs.	Daylight	Warm-white	Natural
Fluorescent tubes (mains-voltage, hot-cathode type)	15 W	1	1	2,500	—	28	25
	20 W	2	$1\frac{1}{2}$	2,500	—	31	28
	30 W	$1\frac{1}{2}$	1	2,500	—	40	36
	30 W	3	1	2,500	—	40	36
	40 W	2	$1\frac{1}{2}$	2,500	—	29	26
	40 W	4	$1\frac{1}{2}$	3,000	45	45	38
	80 W	5	$1\frac{1}{2}$	3,000	40	40	36
End caps all bi-pin except 80 W and 125 W	125 W	8	$1\frac{1}{2}$	3,000	—	—	39

* The large variation in efficiency is primarily because of the different sizes of tube.

Type	Description	A: ft.	B: in.	hrs.	Average lumens per watt throughout life*
Fluorescent tubes, high-voltage, cold-cathode type. Special end caps	250 W	$8\frac{1}{2}$	$\frac{3}{4}$	10,000	31 L/W for 'daylight', 'intermediate white', or 'warm white' colours
Mercury-vapour discharge lamp	80 W			2,500	31
	125 W			2,500	34
	250 W			3,000	32
	400 W			3,000	36
Sodium-vapour discharge lamp	45 W			3,000	49
	60 W			3,000	57
	85 W			3,000	64
	140 W			3,000	64

harsh and irritating. Therefore, in most installations it will be found desirable to use both large and small sources.

With incandescent sources alone, harsh shadows are softened by light reflected from the ceiling and walls if these are light-coloured and well lit. With fluorescent lighting, reflected light is less valuable in this respect; in fact, the light from fluorescent tubes is commonly too diffuse and the addition of point sources will be an advantage to accentuate fine details, as on cloth or silver, or to promote more stimulating conditions.

The light from tungsten and fluorescent sources mixes well, but the colour of the incandescent source itself is unpleasant when juxtaposed with fluorescent tubes and it is important to screen them well from view with opaque shades or louvres so that both *sources* are never seen simultaneously.

At this stage, the requirements of a general-purpose installation can be stated. The ceiling and walls must be well-lighted, otherwise the fittings will seem too bright. This will provide diffuse downward light. The work should be lighted preferentially to focus interest and develop good vision. Some direct light is important to give clarity of detail, and sparkle. The sources themselves should be screened from view, or be reduced in brightness.

A general-purpose fitting to meet these requirements will combine the following features (see Fig. 9):

(1) The fitting should not be close to the ceiling; a pendant fitting is best. A ceiling-mounted fitting cannot light the ceiling adequately because, at low angles, light will glance off even matt surfaces leaving the ceiling dark. It will also accentuate surface irregularities.

(2) The fitting should emit light upward. Light-coloured floors and work surfaces will, of course, reflect a lot of light back onto the ceiling, but generally not less than 15–25 per cent of the light should go up. In buildings like factories where the floor is dark or dirty, as much as 50–60 per cent of upward light may be necessary. The need for upward light can be gauged from the development of fluorescent trough fittings since the war. At first, no light was emitted upwards; next there came a few slots along the top of the fitting, followed by glazed side panels and now to-day the complete reflector is often in translucent material.

(3) The brightness of the source must be reduced and the angle of cut-off must not be less than 40 degrees; greater angles up to 60 degrees are more desirable. The cut-off of many fittings in use to-day does not exceed 20 degrees. For factories this is the minimum allowed by the regulations.

(4) The fitting must emit light sideways to light the walls and will therefore tend necessarily to be rather bright; thus, as a further safeguard against the risk of glare, the brightness at the edge of the fitting should be less than that at its centre, thereby grading the fitting into its surroundings.

Few fittings make use of contrast grading. The Building Research Station has recently developed several fittings to test the principle. One, described later –

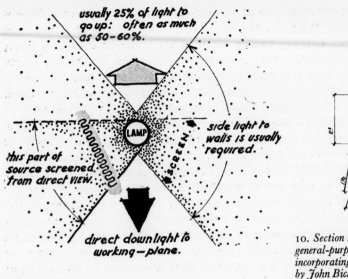

usually 25% of light to go up: often as much as 50–60%.

side light to walls is usually required.

this part of source screened from direct VIEW.

SCREEN

LAMP

direct down light to working-plane.

9. *Diagram of the essential features of good, general-purpose light fittings.*

10. *Section through a B.R.S.-type general-purpose fluorescent fitting, incorporating control-gear, designed by John Bickerdike. The sheet-metal cross-louvres through which the fluorescent tube is threaded are slotted to carry opal perspex side-louvres.*

in the section on hospitals – employs opal perspex shaped to produce the grading effect; another, shown in Fig. 41, uses clear Crinothene, a dimpled and slightly milky plastic which has inherent contrast grading qualities. Ribbed or prismatic glass, or wicker-work can produce similar effects.

Another B.R.S. fitting shown in Fig. 38 admirably satisfies most of the requirements of a general-purpose fluorescent fitting. It is simple, elegant and seems to appeal to architects; it can be manufactured cheaply and can be taken to pieces for easy packaging or cleaning. (Fig. 40.) The control gear is located separately. Another fitting developed on very similar lines is shown in Fig. 10: it incorporates the control gear and slightly less light is emitted upwards because of this.

Indirect Lighting. The growth of popularity of indirect lighting coincides with the development of modern lighting sources. Essentially it is a naïve architectural solution to the problem of how to handle the intolerably uncomfortable brightness of filament lamps: they are put right out of sight! It solves one problem but ignores all others.

The method is inefficient because light is lost in reflection from the ceiling, and efficiency falls as the decoration ages and soils. But much the most critical defect is that the upper regions of a room become brighter than the lower regions. This causes the eyes to adapt themselves upwards, making the lower half of the room seem thoroughly underlit and preventing things in it being seen clearly. As a large source, it destroys all shadows, contrast and sparkle; it is soporific and is often used most inaptly for lecture halls causing sleepiness

31

instead of alertness, distraction instead of concentration. The advent of fluorescent tubes has given the fashion a new impetus as they lend themselves more readily to smooth and uniform ceiling illumination. The character of many existing indirect installations would be greatly improved by adding direct point sources to give sparkle and clarity, and to build up the illumination levels.

Totally indirect lighting is quite unsuitable for most environments. It aims at closely integrating lighting and architecture, but it is poorly conceived.

Direct Lighting from Ceiling Fittings. The major problem with ceiling or ceiling recessed fittings is to prevent glare from the fittings, because of the difficulty of lighting the ceiling adequately. If the fittings are recessed, direct lighting of the ceiling from them is clearly impossible. Ceiling fittings have architectural advantages, and in rooms with low ceilings the choice is inevitable.

The major problem is to prevent glare: solutions depend a great deal on the amount of light reflected back onto the ceiling from the surroundings, particularly from the floor. The lightness of the floor may be under the designer's control, but there are many situations where the floor is dark, as in factories, or where the designer himself may wish to use a dark floor. The following points are important when lighting directly from the ceiling:

(*a*) All sources should be better screened than usual. Incandescent sources need more careful screening than fluorescent because they are brighter.

(*b*) Even if the sources are well screened, the fittings themselves are potential sources of glare and it may be necessary to darken their inner surfaces, i.e. louvres or screens and the parts of internal reflecting surfaces which are easily seen from below. In small fittings these surfaces are closer to lamps than in large ones and will have to be darker; more light is then lost in the fitting; hence a large fitting is generally more efficient than a small one.

(*c*) Reduction of the fitting's brightness is more necessary when the floor and walls are dark in colour.

(*d*) Because good screening of the source is necessary, the distribution of light will be constricted. Consequently the fittings should be more closely spaced to obtain good distribution of light and to prevent unrelieved shadowing. This will be less necessary with fluorescent sources.

(*e*) The most efficient ceiling fittings have 'specular' or polished reflectors which direct the light downwards within the confines of the desired angles of cut-off. Such surfaces seen from normal angles (outside the cut-off) are comfortably bright because they tend to assume the brightness of the surroundings rather than that of the source.

(*f*) Adequate direct lighting of walls from ceiling fittings is difficult without bright fittings which *a priori* are inadmissible. Thus unless the floor is light enough supplementary lighting of the walls will be necessary either from directional fittings in the periphery of the ceiling or from floor standards.

(*g*) If the fitting is well screened the ceiling can be dark in colour with little risk of glare.

(*h*) Very small, bright point sources of light may be used to give sparkle without discomfort. Generally they should be widely spaced, especially in a large ceiling.

Fig. 35 shows a large twin-tube fitting designed to fit the 2 ft. module of a ceiling panel heating system.

Generally, all ceiling-mounted installations will be considerably less efficient than pendant installations.

'*Louverall*' *Ceilings.* Many of the problems which arise by using ceiling fittings are circumvented by a new type of installation called the louverall ceiling in which the whole ceiling is composed of crossing louvres in an egg-crate-like arrangement. The light sources are above the louvres which are usually formed to a cut-off of 45 degrees in cells 2 × 2 × 2 in. deep. The development of louver-all ceilings is linked with that of fluorescent tubes since only with large area sources is it easy to light the louvres uniformly. Given a white ceiling or diffusing reflectors above the lamps the installation has an efficiency of approximately 60 per cent of that for unlouvred direct fittings; this can be raised to 75 per cent with specular reflectors. The fluorescent lamps are normally fitted in continuous lines spaced between one and a half and three times their distance above the louvres. The louvres are usually made up in panels two to three feet square and fixed to ribs suspended from the ceiling. (Figs. 11, 48, 48a.)

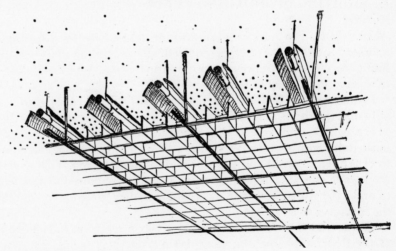

11. *The louverall type of ceiling.*

As a louverall ceiling tends to be brighter than the lower region of a room it can have some of the defects of an indirectly lighted ceiling, but, unlike the latter, its brightness may be reduced by merely darkening the louvres; some

C

light will be lost, of course, the dark louvres absorbing light which they would otherwise have reflected. This technique of controlling the brightness of the source is not often employed; even so there is much to be said for it. White louvres will almost always be uncomfortable, and pale greys are probably much better. Opal perspex louvres are sometimes used; they have good characteristics and high efficiency and give better wall illumination.

The depth, spacing and layout pattern of a louverall ceiling may, of course, be varied provided the cut-off angles are maintained. Scale effect should be borne in mind; small cells will be well defined locally but will disappear in the distance. Big cells are as effective as small ones; they are probably also cheaper and easier to maintain.

The cost of a louverall ceiling is many times that of a normal installation of fittings but in new buildings much of this will be offset by the louvres taking the place of a normal finished ceiling.

In America where the louverall ceiling is common, trouble has been experienced from glare reflected from work surfaces. This is affecting the use of such ceilings in offices and other buildings where the work is visual on a horizontal surface. It is used extensively in entrances and other spaces in which no visual work is done.

4. LIGHTING OF BUILDING TYPES

Factories

Natural Light. The three most important lighting factors affecting the design of a factory are the area of glass required, the control on glare and the control on sunlight. While it is necessary to separate these factors for close examination they have ultimately to be integrated.

In single-storey factories the commonest forms of roof-lighting are the north light and the equal-pitch roof with continuous bands, or dispersed units, of glass. It is now generally agreed that the traditional north light is unsatisfactory for most industries because, in lighting from one direction, only one side of the work is adequately lit and the other side is in the shade. This tends to determine the layout of plant, or else the work is badly shadowed. Shadowing also tends to make the work areas look dirty whether they are clean or not, and to reduce the incentive to be clean.

The north light usually has an excessively large area of glass (up to 40 per cent of the floor area) and the view down a factory, facing the glass, presents a vista of bright sky to which the eye adapts itself at the expense of good vision in the darker work areas. The glitter of light reflected from polished or oily surfaces adds to the already unpleasant effect. The distribution of light is seldom uniform as it tends to drop sharply under the valley of the roof.

The north-light roof has been favoured in the past because it excludes sunlight. While it is still essential to prevent the sun's heat or glare being a nuisance,

34

factory people now no longer have a pronounced Victorian aversion to sunlight and there is a tendency to put small south lights in existing roofs to secure both cross-lighting and sunlight. A quarter to one-third of the north-light area is generally adequate. If the glass is at the base of the slope it will be shadowed most of the year, so excluding direct sunlight.

Shafts of sunlight which throw glaring patches of brightness on the work can be prevented by using diffusing glass, but then there is always the danger that the glass itself will be uncomfortably bright. The choice of glass is usually limited to the wired varieties which behave fairly well in these circumstances.

The desire for freedom in laying out production lines may have led to the early use in American factories of the Monitor type roof. The glass usually faced east-west to cut out most of the sun, but illumination levels were low and incorrect proportions of 'high' and 'low' bays gave uneven light distribution: because only limited areas of sky were visible from any single point glare was reduced.

It was with these problems in mind that the Building Research Station recently designed an asymmetrical monitor roof combining the good features of the normal monitor and the north light. It faces north-south, not east-west, and gives good light distribution and much higher illumination levels than the normal monitor. Good cross-ventilation of the roof space is possible so that the roof is eminently suitable for such buildings as foundries and steel rolling mills. All glazing can be readily cleaned from the outside, or from an internal cleaning cradle.

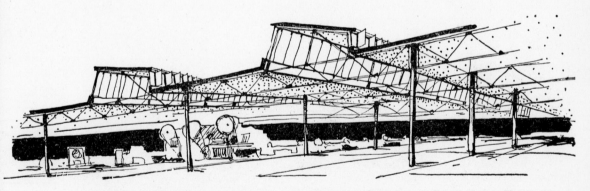

12. *A B.R.S.-type asymmetrical monitor roof used on the Sigmund Pump Factory, Gateshead-upon-Tyne. (Architects: Yorke, Rosenberg & Mardall.)*

The equal-pitch roof gives high levels of illumination; it is cheap, but is very exposed to sunlight and cleaning the glass is difficult. It is not uncommon in this and the north-light type of factory to find glass transmission values as low as 50 per cent because of dirt; in particularly dirty areas or industries the transmission may drop to as low as 10 per cent. Also, in the equal-pitch type of roof, the glass is fully in view from all points, causing visual discomfort and disability; and, unless it is screened, say by louvres or by the structure itself, this type of roof is acceptable only for rough work.

The modern practice of dispersing glazing about the roof in small units rather than in continuous bands is unfortunate, because the pattern of strong contrasts they create accentuates the glare effects causing discomfort and irritation.

Horizontal Glazing for Roofs. The amount of light contributed by horizontally positioned glass is at least double that from vertical glazing of the same area; this accounts for the low illumination levels of monitor roofs, and in effect it means that less fenestration is necessary at low pitches. With the glazing flat, it should be possible to halve the normal area of glass, i.e. about 10 or 15 per cent of the floor area compared with the normal 25–40 per cent. The advantages of less glazing are: (i) reduced heat losses; (ii) reduced heat gains (though, of course, some sunlight can penetrate freely); (iii) reduced glare effects, since the area of source is less; (iv) less maintenance in cleaning glass. Fig. 13 shows the

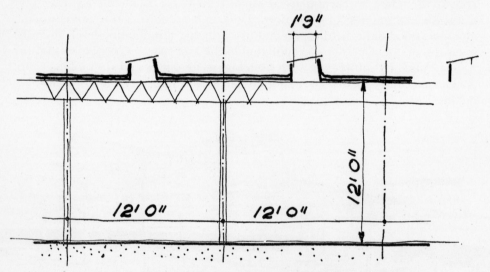

13. *Cross-section through the workshops for the proposed Luton Technical College: the small area of near-horizontal roof-glass is used in narrow strips. (Architects: Norman and Dawbarn.)*

design of the workshops for the proposed Luton Technical College in which the glass area has been reduced to 12 per cent of the floor area; the glass is distributed in narrow strips over a flat roof and the depth of surround and the narrowness of the glazing strip provide a natural cut-off to the glass, making louvering unnecessary. Normal rough-cast glass will diffuse the sunlight and the deep surround will reduce the risk of glare from the brightly flashing glass.

There is much in favour of a trend toward this kind of roof treatment for factories, particularly small ones, because initial costs, maintenance costs and heat losses are likely to be low.

Windows, even whole window walls, in large factories, generally contribute very little useful direct light because penetration is slight. Also, if the work is viewed against them they may cause discomfort and prevent proper vision. But most people enjoy a view to the outside and therefore windows should be designed primarily for this purpose. They should be made comfortable to look at by keeping down contrasts and by restricting the area of visible sky. Low window heads and sills and external planting all help in this respect. Since wall space is generally very useful in factories, individual large windows, widely spaced, are likely to be more acceptable than a string of openings occupying a whole wall; also the latter is likely to be more glaring.

The completely windowless factory has not been accepted in this country as it has in America. The Americans argue that installation costs for artificial light are the same either way and that roof glazing merely adds to heating costs. With no experience over here it is difficult to say whether or not modern artificial lighting at the levels used in America (50–100 L/sq. ft.) is an adequate substitute for natural light. Department Stores manage without it of course, but is a building without visible contact with the outside world aesthetically acceptable? Almost certainly it is not. One compromise solution which the Americans are finding successful is the vision-strip window in the outer walls of the factory. Another likely solution may be to drop small glazed patios into the central areas of workshops.

Artificial Light. Standards of artificial lighting in factories are poor at present. Most industrial fittings are designed to get the maximum light onto the working plane irrespective of visual comfort. The chief faults are poor screening of the lamp and little or no upward light. Existing regulations do little to encourage well-designed fittings. They specify a minimum cut-off of 20 degrees with the consequence that most fittings are designed down to this in an effort to distribute light sideways to avoid shadowing. The cut-off should be at least 40 degrees, and up to 60 degrees is desirable. Spread of light sideways can be obtained by making the fitting of a translucent material dense enough to prevent the part nearest the lamp from being unduly bright.

The amount of upward light depends on the proportion of light reflected onto the ceiling from the work and the floor; reflection will be low in a foundry and high in a weaving shed handling light-coloured cloth and having light floors. Experience has shown that for average conditions in a machine shop not less than 25 per cent should go up. All of this light is not lost of course, for if the ceiling is light-coloured, as it should be, most of the upward light is reflected back onto the work and helps to soften shadows and reduce contrasts on the work. The lighting of the whole environment, especially the roof surfaces, is the first step towards good visual conditions and the creation of stimulating and gloom-free surroundings.

It is now thought that a combination of fluorescent and incandescent sources is best in factories. The advantages of mixing the two sources have been discussed earlier in this chapter. The Building Research Station recently demonstrated the effectiveness of this method in the lighting of a weaving shed near Oldham. The fittings used are shown in Fig. 36 and Fig. 37. The fluorescent fittings contain two 80 watt 5 ft. tubes, and conform with the principles set out earlier. They give good general illumination of between 20 and 25 L/sq. ft. on the looms, which in this case is raised to 32–38 L/sq. ft. by the tungsten fittings. The tungsten fittings are most unobtrusive because the lamp is highly screened and the spread of light tightly restricted. Operatives confirm that cloth detail is easier to see. However, the benefits obtained seem out of all proportion to the mere increase of illumination; the contrasts produced on the cloth, and in the environment generally, appear to help maintain attention and alertness, especially on the night shift. The whole weaving shed has been treated comprehensively in colour, lighting and noise reduction and is fully described in a paper *The Lighting of Buildings* by Allen and Hopkinson.*

Recent developments in the tungsten ballast lamp units for fluorescent tubes should result in a greater use of mixed systems; a special tungsten filament lamp serves as ballast and the whole arrangement is likely to be cheaper than the fluorescent fittings alone.

Directional lighting for the work can, of course, come from local fittings mounted near the work. But, while they are necessary for certain tasks, they are usually poorly designed or wrongly fixed, and are often stripped-out in favour of high value general lighting. There is need for a well-designed, robust local fitting which is easily adjusted, because even with good general lighting there will always be work which cannot be done without such a fitting, for example boring and grinding.

Cold-cathode lighting is not often used in this country, except decoratively. Fig. 46 shows a recent installation in a shipbuilder's new drawing office. It has a shell concrete roof and the architect naturally wished to keep its clean form and outline free of suspended fittings. This led to the decision to use lamps close to the ceiling contrary to what is normally advisable; in this particular case however there is so much light reflected back to the vaults from white paper, light-coloured benches and clean floors, that the contrast between tubes and roof is acceptable, even though the tubes are unscreened; also, the surface brightness of cold-cathode tubes is slightly less than that of normal fluorescent tubes.

The elimination of fittings off-sets the higher costs of this type of source. Cold-cathode tubes were chosen because their long life and their reliability reduce maintenance – an important consideration when the tubes are in inaccessible positions. The design of the lighting was closely integrated with the sound-

* See Bibliography.—Ed.

38

absorbent treatment – panels of perforated hardboard backed with glass silk quilt. The bulky control gear for the lamps is located behind these panels. Spot-lights, similar to those used in the weaving shed described earlier, are fixed to the panels to give sharpness and sparkle to the lighting and to improve its colour rendering.

An advanced trend in artificial lighting is the use of trunking systems onto which the tubes and reflectors are fixed: the trunks span freely between trusses and need supporting only at about 12–15 ft. intervals. Suspension chains and cables are eliminated, all the wiring and gear is totally enclosed, and other small service lines can be carried. In American factories, where illumination levels are high, between 50 and 100 L/sq. ft., the tubes are ranged continuously along the trunking in banks of two, three or four lines. In this country where levels are seldom more than 30 L/sq. ft. the tubes are generally well spaced out in two lines.

Lighting and colour cannot be divorced: in factories, colour has a large part to play in determining comfort conditions in addition to its aesthetic qualities. The *brightness* of a surface results from the illumination of that surface and its reflection factor. Many factories have found that light colours for walls are generally undesirable because the walls are then usually brighter than the work itself. The background should of course be darker than the work. In the weaving shed previously discussed, colours with reflection factors as low as 20 per cent have been used, often in fully saturated hues. All surfaces seen near sources of light, natural or artificial, should have high reflection factors to reduce contrast, i.e. whites on glazing bars, roofs and trusses.

Hospitals
Natural Lighting. At the present time the whole problem of hospital design is under review by the Nuffield Provincial Hospitals Trust, which has set up the Investigation into the Functions and Design of Hospitals under the directorship of an architect. One of the many subjects they are studying is the lighting of wards.

In Great Britain the design of wards has changed very little since – almost a hundred years ago – Florence Nightingale's precise recommendations for the layout, shape and sizes of wards became standard.

Daylight and sunlight in wards have a direct germicidal action, and a well-lit room will be kept cleaner. Good lighting is also required for many nursing and medical procedures, and it has a beneficial psychological effect on patients and staff. The provision of high levels of natural illumination implies large windows, and it is at this point that the real troubles arise in the day-lighting of wards. Hospital patients are in a hypersensitive state and are particularly susceptible to glare. Poorly designed windows, especially those showing a large area of sky to the patient lying in bed, can cause severe discomfort. This happens in the traditional English ward where the patient lies at right angles to the outside wall facing tall windows from which he can get little relief by turning to one side or the other; nor can he have the pleasure of looking out of the windows flanking his bed, as they are behind him.

Abroad, the system known as the Rigs layout is common. The beds are parallel to the outer walls, usually two deep on one side of the gangway and one on the other side. The chief advantages of this layout are that it allows a thicker and more compact building and thereby economizes in walking distance, heating, site utilization, and so on. But with the thicker block arises the problem of obtaining sufficient daylight penetration to light effectively the centre of the blocks. Will the additional ceiling height needed to light the centre of the ward be so great as to offset the other economies? Can windows be designed which will be comfortable for the patients adjacent to them?

To find the answers to these questions and others the Nuffield Trust and the Building Research Station constructed a model of a section of ward and arranged artificial skies to reproduce natural lighting conditions. The conclusions to date are:

(a) If light-coloured decorations are used, the light measured at certain points in the centre of the ward will be as much as seven or eight times as great as the calculated *sky factor*, which is the figure for direct light. This emphasizes the great importance of reflected light. The floor and ceiling were shown to contribute most of the reflected light and consequently they should always be light in colour. The walls contributed less and any individual wall made only a small contribution to the whole. Darker colours may therefore be used on limited areas of walls.

(b) That although increasing the window height produces a proportional increase in the direct light (sky factor) it does not cause anything like a proportionate increase of the total daylight when the contribution of reflected light is added. This is because the windows in the opposite wall let light escape and so reduce the integrating effect of the room. The windows act, in fact, as black walls.

(c) That windows running down to the floor allow the floor near the window to be well lit, instead of being shadowed by a sill wall, and this, coupled with extra light reflected from the ground outside, makes a substantial contribution to the level of illumination deep in the room.

(d) That a horizontal fin or louvre in the windows could be designed to cut off the view of sky from the beds nearest to the windows while permitting light to penetrate freely to the centre of the ward.

(e) That even with the loss of light caused by the fin, it was found that a ward building 43 ft. wide would be adequately lit with a ceiling height of 10 ft.

Artificial Lighting. Inefficiently screened lamps and strong contrasts readily cause acute irritation and discomfort especially to patients who cannot move in bed. Well-screened fittings, giving a soft, even light on the walls and ceiling, are of first importance therefore. The Building Research Station recently designed a fitting to conform with these requirements (Fig. 39). To light the walls, part of the fitting has generally to be bright: the B.R.S. fitting aims at overcoming the effect of discomfort by grading the brightness gradually into the surroundings; hence the shape of the fitting. The open base allows the ward gangway to be lit preferentially, while screening the lamp from patient's view. In the centre of the opening is a small reflector holding a 15-watt night lamp. The fitting should be particularly suitable for the traditional type of ward with a fairly high ceiling.

About the characteristics for lighting sick wards little is known for certain beyond the comfort requirements. But it is generally agreed by the medical profession that a restful and near-soporific environment is desirable. This requirement will be satisfied by general low-level lighting, but in modern low-ceiling wards it is often difficult to light the ceilings properly as fittings cannot be suspended far enough away from them. The Building Research Station is starting to investigate this problem: so far they have two lines of approach. One is to study the merits of specially designed standard lamps for the general lighting, and the other is to study highly screened ceiling-lights which spread little light directly sideways but, by strongly lighting the floor beneath the fitting, illuminate the remainder of the ward by reflection. The general level of illumination should be low – about three lumens per sq. ft. is adequate for normal nursing.

In addition there should be a bedside adjustable fitting with a long-reach arm for clinical examination. The shades of the present types need modification to give a better cut-off to the lamp. About 60 degrees of cut-off is the minimum if patients in opposite beds are not to suffer discomfort.

Not quite the same characteristics are required in convalescent wards, although comfortable glare-free lighting is still necessary. Stimulating environmental conditions are likely to encourage recovery, and soporific lighting is therefore undesirable. Sparkle and a certain amount of contrast in the lighting will be helpful, for there is little doubt that such conditions help to induce a healthy attitude of mind. A focus of interest, such as a mural decoration, to encourage alertness may be useful, and lighting should not be divorced from the other attributes of an interior, such as colour, texture and pattern.

Schools
Natural Light. The regulations of the 1944 Education Act prescribe a minimum Daylight Factor (Sky Factor in reality) of 2 per cent for teaching rooms with a recommendation that a higher figure of up to 5 per cent should be secured if possible. Briefly the 2 per cent figure is intended for existing and multi-storey schools where side-lighting only is possible and the 5 per cent is for single-storey schools where clerestory or top-lighting can be introduced. The objective of this high standard was to safeguard against inadequate lighting as the probable cause of the steady deterioration in vision which occurs in children during their

school life. Its major effect is to reduce glare by reducing the overall contrast between indoor and outdoor brightnesses.

The first schools built to the 5 per cent S.F. minimum had window walls between 12 and 14 ft. high – a glass area of some 50 per cent of the floor area in one wall. But such room heights were uneconomical and out of scale with children, and the ingenuity of the architect was tested in devising different forms of fenestration to reduce them. The first move was to bi-lateral lighting – chiefly to a clerestory over the corridor which brought ceiling heights down to 10 or 11 ft. To-day, 8-ft. ceiling heights are possible with the use of top-lights. At first the efficiency of top-lights was greatly underestimated; areas as much as one-third of the floor area were used and elaborate costly treatments were devised to cut down both sky and sun glare. The cost of these top-lights off-set the economy of the lower ceiling. In the latest schools the area of the top-light has been reduced to about 5 per cent of the floor area and is so small that the depth of surround gives all the visual screening necessary (up to 30 or 40 degrees) and louvres are eliminated. This combined with the low window-heads – about 7 ft. 6 in. – and the even distribution of light makes the rooms particularly comfortable visually. The 'natural' screening of the roof light together with diffusing glass prevents glare from the sun. Another form of top-lighting is seen in Fig. 27. The roof trusses are filled in to form deep louvres, and side windows are chiefly for vision.

Another development is the frequent use of lighting from two adjacent sides often combined with a clerestory. This again allows low ceilings and reduces contrasts. It suggests, too, the solution to the problem of lighting multi-storey schools with classrooms on either side of a spine corridor. Here again the basic difficulty is to obtain sufficient penetration of light without uneconomically high ceilings. By the acceptance of a serrated plan and a slightly irregular lay-out of rooms, particularly at the ends of the wings, it is possible to obtain light from two and sometimes three directions and thus meet the 2 per cent regulation with a ceiling height at least as low as 10 ft. and probably less.

Various devices are used in schools to reduce the discomforting effects of sky glare and sun glare. It is important to distinguish between the two effects because they seldom occur together. The blue sky on a sunny day is low in brightness, therefore sun glare is the problem; the condition of an overcast sky which is common in this country is without sun glare but sky glare can be most uncomfortable, often more so than sun glare because of its large area.

Generally it has been found that translucent blinds, roller or pleated, control sky glare best without too severe a reduction in illumination levels. The metal venetian type of blind is almost as good at reducing sky glare but the slats tend to be more contrasty; by careful manipulation, however, daylight can be distributed better with this than with any other type of blind. It is about 25 per cent more expensive.

Both linen and venetian blinds give excellent control over summer and winter sunlight – the venetian type is slightly better, but neither prevents the entry of solar heat, although they do both *diffuse* it so that it is never concentrated at any one place in the room. Only external treatments can prevent or reduce heat penetration. Canvas blinds of the shop front or Italian type successfully deal with the heat of the high-angle summer sun but they sharply reduce the day-lighting within a few feet of the window; a more translucent fabric would largely overcome this defect. Slatted screens at lintel level have been used with moderate success. Internal blinds are useful at night in that they prevent loss of artificial light through the window and prevent strong contrasts between the fitting and the 'dark' glass.

A more substantial form of window screening has been used in the main hall of the new Commercial High School at Helsinki (Fig. 31). Here, swivelling, perforated, plywood panels filled with glass silk serve the triple purpose of black-out, sun and sky glare control, and acoustic control.

Artificial Light. The regulations lay down a minimum standard of 12 L/sq. ft. for teaching rooms, a reliable figure based on recent research. The character of the lighting should be stimulating to maintain alertness yet free of any disabling qualities which might make easy and comfortable seeing difficult over long periods.

In general, good all-round illumination is required to prevent strong contrasts with the fittings. The major part of the light should be directed on the desks, the teacher and the chalkboard, with perhaps slight emphasis on the chalkboard to focus attention.

Most opal fittings are unsuitable because of their high surface brightness and because they do not preferentially light the most important parts of the room. Fittings such as that shown in Fig. 41 have the right characteristics: a good cut-off to the lamp (about 60 degrees), plenty of upward light, light for the walls and pin-ups and a large enough shade to give the fitting a low brightness. The material used is Crinothene, which sparkles and gives about the right degree of stimulation and contrast grading.

The problem of lighting the ceiling with closely-mounted fittings has yet to be solved in practice. One line of approach is to form the ceiling in slopes or curves so that light reaches it at reasonable angles (Fig. 14a). Another is to employ fittings in which contrast grading is well-developed. The hospital ward fitting in Fig. 39, previously discussed, has this characteristic but it is lacking in sparkle so vital for teaching rooms. The problem is at present under investigation by the B.R.S.

Art Galleries

In art galleries and museums, lighting is the dominant force in design; it influences all features of design, from the natural lighting arrangements in the roof to details such as surface finish. Until recently the criteria of gallery lighting had not been adequately assessed and unfortunately few if any existing galleries,

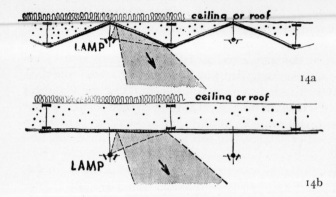

14a. *An arrangement which ensures a bright ceiling without hanging a lighting fitting very far below it.* 14b. *The light fitting has to be hung some distance down to light a flat ceiling reasonably well.*

even recent ones, are examples of successful lighting design. With present knowledge of visual behaviour and illumination principles, architects now have the opportunity of producing highly-refined solutions.

Natural Lighting. The worst defect of present galleries is poor brightness distribution. Thus in top-lighted rooms the pictures are invariably in the worst-lighted zone because the upper parts of the walls usually get more light than the lower parts. This higher brightness above the pictures raises the adaptation level of the eyes causing the paintings to seem relatively dull and dark. In addition, of course, the eyes are distracted and effort is needed to maintain interest on the paintings.

Similar effects are caused, often with noticeably greater severity, when the rooflight is exposed to view. Views of brilliant sky through it are uncomfortable and make the viewing of the paintings even more difficult; conditions are aggravated when the indoor and outdoor brightness differences are increased or when the skylight is surrounded with dark or unlit surfaces. Experience suggests that this last condition is largely responsible for gloominess in galleries and museums with top-lights.

The design of top-lighted rooms should be derived from two major principles: one, that the paintings should hang in the strongest light; the other, that the brightness of the other surfaces in view should not be greater, and should preferably be a little less, than that of the paintings.

The first principle demands an accurate control of daylight distribution on the walls; and the second, rooflight screening. A successful design will admit light preferentially to the lower parts of the walls without allowing big areas of sky to come within view. This has been the basis of several gallery designs, notably the Boymans Museum at Rotterdam (Fig. 32), and the Museum at Linköping, Sweden. Unfortunately until recently it was not practical to compute daylight distribution nor was the principle of preferential distribution fully recognized, so faulty roof arrangements have to be expected.

The Building Research Station has recently devised a treatment for existing

44

galleries in the City Gallery, Birmingham, based on these principles. A cross section of the design is shown in Fig. 15, and Fig. 33 is a photograph of the interior of the model used extensively in the development of the design. The projecting cove was formed to obstruct some light from the upper parts of the walls without reducing picture illumination, and the false ceiling or velarium partly spanning the room screens direct views of the rooflight. If the velarium is raised, its width must be reduced, and if it is lowered the width can be increased without disturbing the wall illumination. The velarium alone does not completely screen the view of sky and a single louvre was inserted over the gap to complete the screening without affecting the picture illumination. The cut-off is effective from all positions greater than 8 ft. 6 in. from the pictures, which is a normal viewing position for spectators. In the actual gallery, the velarium is likely to be built up of small opaque crossing louvres formed like an egg-crate, so that while views of the rooflight are screened, light can penetrate to the centre of the room; the brightness of the louvres is controlled by colouring them so that their brightness can be related to the rest of the room.

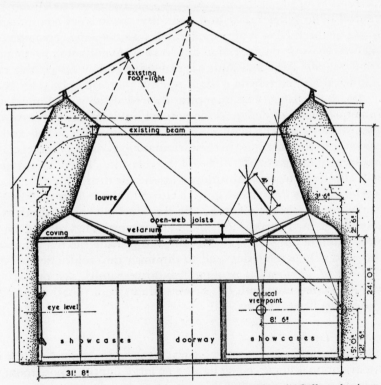

15. *Cross-section of the proposed alterations to the Birmingham Art Gallery, showing suggestions made by B.R.S. for modifying the top-lighting.*

45

Another stage in developing good viewing conditions is to assess the reflection factors desirable for all the surfaces in the room since brightness distribution depends not only on the light reaching surfaces but also on what they can reflect back. This led the B.R.S. to measure the reflection factors of many paintings and the results show surprisingly that some 90 per cent of paintings in a collection are likely to have reflection factors of under 25 per cent and that the bulk of these will have reflection factors of between 15 and 25 per cent. On the basis that the background brightness to a picture (the object of attention) should be slightly less than that of the picture itself, a value of 20 per cent reflection factor was adopted for the walls in the Birmingham Gallery design. For the other surfaces in view which were differently illuminated, appropriate factors were chosen to adjust their brightness to about that of the wall, or slightly less than that, i.e. low reflection factors for more strongly lighted surfaces and *vice versa*.

Reflections in Glass. No acceptable way is known of overcoming reflections in picture glass; the problem is geometrically insuperable. The real solution is to avoid glass and employ air conditioning in galleries. The first concern of a Director is to preserve his paintings and it is now recognized that only strict control of air temperature and humidity can prevent continuous deterioration of old pictures. Glass is only moderately successful in keeping pictures clean and may cause worse deterioration due to lack of ventilation to the painting and to condensation. Air conditioning is expensive and an alternative may be to draw in filtered air and rely on a slight positive pressure to keep the room clean.

Artificial Lighting. The minimum desired value is 15 lumens per sq. ft. The same principles of design as for natural lighting apply to artificial lighting in picture galleries. The main sources should be well screened and directed from above onto the paintings; in the Birmingham Gallery proposals fluorescent tubes are located along the outer edge of the velarium. The other surfaces in the room will also be lit to maintain proper brightness distribution.

Hot-cathode fluorescent sources either of the 'colour matching' type (colour temperature approx. 6,500°K.) or the 'daylight' or 'natural' type (4,500°K.) have been used successfully in picture rooms. They should be mixed with a proportion of tungsten filament lamps to provide the red component necessary for good colour rendering and to diminish the 'cold' effect of the fluorescent. The use of tungsten ballast lamp transformer units (say, one 110-volt, 150-watt tungsten lamp used with two 80-watt fluorescent tubes) is a likely trend in art gallery artificial lighting.

Domestic Lighting

The more open planning of post-war houses has emphasized the inadequacy of the traditional single ceiling light. The large multi-purpose room, characteristic of open planning, usually has areas set aside for dining, sewing, reading, study and the like, and it is not surprising therefore to find that the most noticeable feature of contemporary light fittings is their flexibility and adaptability. There is a wide choice of counterpoised fittings designed to reach out from wall or table; counterbalanced fittings adjustable for height to go over dining or study table (some even have been devised to traverse the ceiling on track to cover more than one area of activity); and, of course, table and floor standard lamps are finding themselves once again in favour. At a recent exhibition in London of domestic light fittings not one out of a total of sixty or more was designed for ceiling hanging.

Unfortunately many recent fittings though admirable for their sculptural qualities (especially unlit!) are most inefficient and expensive; they employ low wattage lamps necessitating many more fittings and power outlets than need be. This tendency is brought on in part by open planning and in part by the difficulty of designing small high-wattage fittings with a low surface brightness. The old-fashioned shade in new guise is still perhaps the simplest, cheapest and best when properly used. Over activity areas a shade about 2 ft. 6 in. above the table is admirable, provided the cut-off to the lamp is good. Beside splashing light onto the work and focussing interest, it lights the ceiling. The shade must, however, be in a dense material for, as it is at eye level, it would otherwise be glaring.

Uniform lighting has no place in the home. Variety, contrast within limits, sparkle and the creation of points of interest and intimacy – all are achieved by local lighting. Generally speaking all lamps should be well screened; opaque shades concentrate light, translucent ones give general light to surrounding areas as well.

In the kitchen, one source only will generally be inadequate since at some places one's body will always shade the work. This argues against central ceiling fittings and for relating the lighting to the work areas. Here as in the living room there is everything to be said for some local lighting: a spotlight on the wall beside the sink, or even a flexible fitting with a radius sufficient to cover several areas such as cooking, preparation and washing up.

In natural lighting much larger windows are being used concurrently with better heating systems and there is a marked trend towards lower sill heights both upstairs and down. These, of course, give better and more comfortable lighting as well as better linkage with the garden. The B.S. Code of Practice on daylight has done much to improve downstairs lighting especially in kitchens of houses and flats where a 2 per cent minimum is recommended.

5. THE FUTURE OF LIGHTING

The trend today is toward refining present methods and ideas, and developing a sensitive understanding of how these affect building design. In many ways lighting is at present divorced from architecture but there is evidence of closer integration. This is illustrated in the following example.

A short while ago when the author was a member of the Building Research Station, a firm of architects* requested advice on the daylighting of a proposed foundry. The problem of 'dirty' industries has always interested the B.R.S.; they believe there is no sound reason why they should be dirty and this was an opportunity to go beyond merely checking the amount of daylight. It was felt that by attention to good lighting, good ventilation, and colour, a foundry could be made a clean place. Ventilation is, of course, the key factor; uncontrolled ventilation allows heat and dirt to be diffused all over the place, even to otherwise clean areas: colour schemes in such an atmosphere quickly lose their effectiveness, the cleaning problem is almost insuperable, and even when good natural lighting is provided at the start it rapidly deteriorates as the glass becomes dirty. Not much is known about heat-flow in foundries, but ventilation and heat-flow almost amount to the same movement; the objective is to control the heat-flow around the hottest processes. In most foundries, the cupolas develop a tremendous flue action which should be turned to advantage. Air-inlets should not be located in their vicinity but in the distant walls so that fresh air will be drawn across the body of the foundry; if the inlets are near the cupolas, the fresh air will short-circuit and dirt and fumes will spread to the rest of the works. Once the air is free of dust and dirt, and not before, attention can be turned to the other provisions. The original proposals for daylighting in this example consisted of a series of monitors which analysis revealed did not give adequate illumination even though the glass area was high (40 per cent of the floor area). A modified form of the B.R.S. monitor roof was suggested; this used the same area of glass but 4 per cent of it was used at a nearly flat pitch in the roof of the monitor (in small panels). The illumination levels were some three times higher than those of the original scheme using the same glass area; the small percentage of horizontal glass contributed almost a quarter of the total illumination.

In the original scheme only the roof was to be of concrete, but it did seem sensible to make the framework and the stanchions also in concrete, as maintenance of steelwork in a corrosive atmosphere is difficult. In co-operation with the architects this led to the development of the structural system shown in Fig. 49. The roof structure is, in effect, a system of large louvres crossing one another which cut off full views of the glazing. The sides of the main beams cant inwards to prevent dirt adhering and the lateral webs act as stiffeners for the main beams.

The artificial sources will be located high in the middle of each cell, and fittings will be dispensed with, for the structural screening makes them redundant. The sources will be serviced and the glazing cleaned from a trolley running on a rail down the centre of each monitor.

The roof space is the only part of a foundry where colour can be applied. It

---

* S. N. Cooke & Partners, Birmingham.

48

16

SCREENING GLARE. 16. *An office building at Los Angeles has on its south façade a cantilevered framing unit containing a* brise-soleil *of vertical aluminium alloy louvres to shade the offices from the bright, hot Californian sun. The* brise-soleil *can be removed in winter. It is lit at night from below by concealed fluorescent tubes. (Architect: Richard Neutra.)*
17. *A* brise-soleil *seen from within: another example from California. In some examples, the slats are movable in order to reflect the maximum amount of light without producing glare while at the same time providing adequate ventilation. In these examples the application is new but the principle is old; the Venetian blind and the slatted shutter of wood are earlier versions on a smaller scale (see fig. 24, p. 51).*

17

18

SCREENING GLARE.
18. *Galerie de Henri II, Fontainebleau, has windows fully screened by massive piers; glare is cut off and the eyes can thus take in all the decorative detailing without undue strain. Moulded surfaces catch the light and distribute it across the room.* 19. *Georgian windows have deep, splayed white-painted reveals, both inside and outside; these, with the narrow, tapered glazing-bars, reduce glare and provide contrast grading of the daylight. The deep reveals also reduce the area of visible, glaring sky.* 20. *Simple, deep, cross louvres in a picture gallery of the Boymans Museum, Rotterdam, cut out glare from the roof glazing (Architect: A. van der Steur).*

20

19

21

22

SCREENING GLARE. *Further examples of reduction of glare by screening the direct daylight.* 21. *A long, side-lit gallery in the Boymans Museum, a modern example of the principle used in the Galerie de Henri II, Fontainebleau.* 22. *Roof beams in the ASEA factory, Västeros, Sweden, act as screens against glare from roof-lights and give evenly distributed reflected light.* 23. *The Assembly Hall of Summerswood School, Boreham Wood, has small top-lights with deep reveals acting as screens against direct sky glare in the same way as do the deep Georgian window reveals on the vertical plane. (Architects: Hertfordshire County Architect: C. H. Aslin.)* 24. *A Dutch window shutter of wood is based on the same screening principle as the modern* brise-soleil *of concrete or aluminium alloy, though the scale is smaller.*

23

24

25

DAYLIGHTING IN SCHOOLS. 25. *Interior of a classroom in a Hertfordshire County Council school having low contrasts due to cross lighting. Here the complete window wall is replaced by a view-window and a clerestory with a panel between. The panel reduces the area of sky seen through the view-window while the clerestories light the panel and so minimize contrasts. 26. Over-large roof lights having elaborate and expensive adjustable louvres in an infants' classroom of a Hertfordshire County Council Primary School (Designers: Arcon). 27. Costs in school buildings are now being reduced by lower ceilings in classrooms as in this example of a Middlesex County Council school where a view-window is supplemented by top lights composed of louvres built around the roof trusses.*

26

27

28   29

SCREENING IN SCHOOLS. *Proper daylighting conditions are particularly important in schools. Here are three examples of louvre screens to control glare.* 28. *A projecting hood at a school in Fresno, California, reduces glare from sun and sky (Architects: David H. Horn and Marshall D. Mortland).* 29. *Louvred corridor lighting at a school in Oregon (Architects: Wilmsen and Endicott).* 30. *Another projecting hood at a Hatfield, Herts., school built of prefabricated aluminium alloy units (Architects: Arcon).*

30

31

32

DAYLIGHT CONTROL WITH LOUVRES.
31. *Movable plywood panels of the hall window of the new Commercial High School, Helsinki, provide sun and sky glare controls, black-out and variable acoustic conditions (Architects: Hugo Harmia and Woldemar Baeckman).*
32. *Small louvres set at an angle of 45 degrees in the ceilings of the main picture rooms of the Boymans Museum, Rotterdam, screen the harsh direct light from the sky.*

LOUVRED ROOF LIGHTING. 33. *A model of the Birmingham City Art Gallery lighting scheme evolved by the Building Research Station. A laylight of louvering allows the light from the sky to fall on the paintings without causing its glare to fall on the visitor's eye (see sectional drawing on p. 45) (Architect: John Bickerdike). 34. Workshop rooflight at Folkestone Technical College. Fibreboard sheathing of the structural roof members prevents glare by screening the North-light and also conceals service pipes (Architects: Kent County Council – S. H. Loweth, Chief Architect.)*

33

34

35

INTEGRATED LIGHTING. 35. *A ceiling fitting using twin 40-watt tubes designed to be incorporated into a patent system of ceiling panel heating on a 2-ft. module at the new chemistry laboratories of Cambridge University (Designer: John Bickerdike; Architects: Easton and Robertson). 36. A twin-tube fluorescent fitting, for fixing to steel trusses, designed by the B.R.S. 37. The same fitting installed in a weaving shed renovated by the B.R.S.*

36

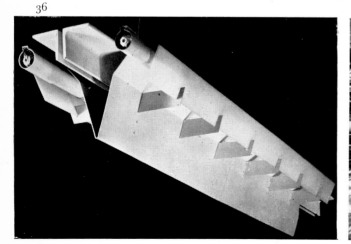

37

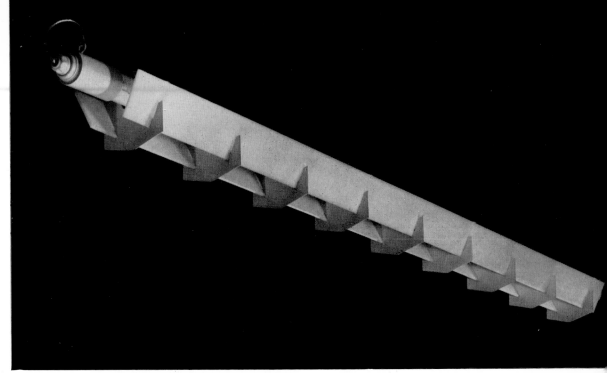

38

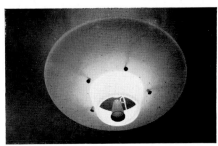

39

40

41

INDIVIDUAL FITTINGS. 38. *A general-purpose fluorescent fitting evolved by the B.R.S. The tube is screened to cut out glare by two translucent slats held at an angle of 40 degrees by lateral louvres threaded onto the tube. An alternative version has the lateral louvres clipped to a small alloy tube from which the suspension and wiring are taken. (40 is the same fitting dismantled, showing that manufacture and packing are simple.) 39. A fitting designed by B.R.S. with good contrast-grading properties and suitable for hospitals. The small cone in the centre is a night-light. 41. A simple general-purpose fitting in clear Crinothene developed by B.R.S. for use with a filament lamp. The bottom is open to allow a downward flood of light, the cut-off being 60 degrees. An inner ring screens the lamp to cut out glare and the main shade is large enough to produce a low surface brightness. Note the contrast grading from the centre to the outer area of the shade.*

42

43

SHOP LIGHTING. 42. *A swivelling spotlight with louvred mouth which is useful for stores and shop windows (Designers: Messrs. Courtney, Pope).* 43. *A shoe shop at Plymouth provides an example of integrated lighting design in which fittings have been recessed in the ceiling (Architect: Ellis Somake).* 44. *Another integrated shop design in a carpet store in New York. Both examples make use of the dramatic, sparkling qualities of artificial lighting with high contrasts in order to attract customers.* 45. *A shoe shop in Bristol provides another example of a contrasty, integrated lighting scheme which includes sunk coffers of indirect light (Architect: Ellis Somake).*

44

45

46

47

INTEGRATED LIGHTING.
46. *The drawing office at Wallsend Shipyard having cold cathode fluorescent tube lighting integrated with acoustic absorbents (Architects: Richard Sheppard and Partners; lighting consultant, John Bickerdike). 47. Indirect lighting in the foyer ceiling of the Royal Festival Hall, London. The ceiling follows the slope of the auditorium floor above and when illuminated can therefore be seen from outside (Architects: R. H. Matthew and J. L. Martin for the L.C.C.).*

48

48a

48. EGG-CRATE CEILINGS. *The ground floor of an office building at Los Angeles. The entire ceiling is composed of an egg-crate grille behind which is set an unbroken series of fluorescent tubes 3 ft. above the grille and providing diffused lighting with complete absence of shadow (Architect: Richard Neutra).*
48a. *Egg-crate type 'Difulite' cellular ceiling lighting panels (Metal Sections Ltd.) made from 2 in. × .010 in. aluminium alloy curved strips in panels up to a maximum of 30 in. × 84 in.*

is valuable therefore to have large, clean, well-lighted surfaces in the roof to provide adequate opportunity to use colour. These surfaces, as they are well lit, also provide the necessary diffusion of both daylight and artificial light to the work areas below.

A similar solution has been developed for the workshops of the new Folkestone Technical College (Fig. 34).

Both these schemes have a common factor: both use structure to screen the

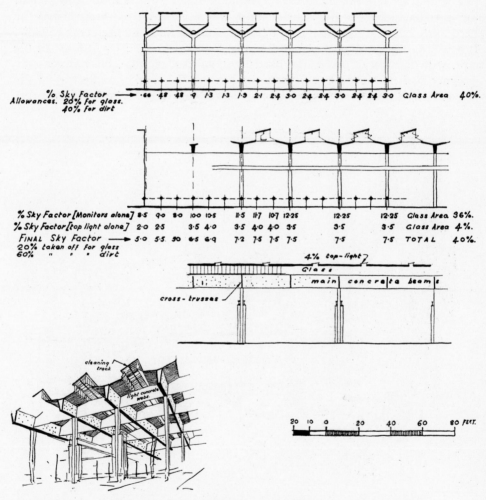

49. *Development of a foundry design. Top: original section. Second from top: section as modified. Next: longitudinal section. Bottom left: perspective sketch.*

light sources in place of applied louvres or fittings. Here, then, is lighting and structure fully integrated. It may be achieved in other ways as shown in the Swedish factory in Fig. 22, or in the plan of the new Cathedral for Coventry.

In all these examples, architects are learning to use structure and the fabric of their building to provide good visual conditions. This may appear to cut across a contemporary aim at clean and uncluttered surface, for example the increasing use of shell roofs – but in fact it carries the aim further; from the desire for tidiness to the logical end of orderliness.

The increase in levels of artificial illumination necessitates more fittings, and the introduction of the fluorescent lamp, which is bulky, has emphasized the need for fully integrating artificial lighting with the building design as a whole. If it is not fully integrated, a building can be overwhelmed by fittings. In the past, with the risk of fire from naked light sources – candle, oil and gas – the designer had no choice but to hang or bracket the sources well clear of the fabric. Also, to compensate for the low candle-power of sources, fittings were

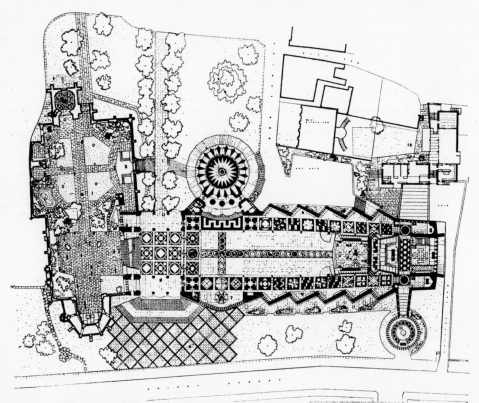

50. *Plan of proposed Coventry Cathedral showing how, in the nave, direct daylight shining into the eyes of the congregation is avoided. Instead, the light is deliberately directed towards the 'hallowing-places' and the High Altar. This might almost be called a form of planned structural louvering. (Architect: Basil Spence.)*

large and consequently figured prominently in design; the multi-point chandelier in fact represents the peak of fittings design. Such constraints no longer operate and installations are now being produced commercially which go part way towards full integration of fabric and sources, for example Louverall ceilings, recessed-type fittings, and, in America, standardized units of acoustic-cum-lighting screens which are hung between bare fluorescent tubes.

★   ★   ★

All aspects of building which are concerned with the senses – heating, lighting and colour, acoustics, and so on – require subtle handling, deep insight into people's behaviour, physical, physiological and emotional, and a balanced interpretation. The aim of the architect is towards an effective synthesis of modern methods, materials and human needs; it must never be forgotten that human needs and feelings are the basic formulative force in design: they thread and link together the material factors. Of all these needs, light has perhaps the widest influence on architecture.

BIBLIOGRAPHY

The Brightness of the Environment and its Influence on Visual Comfort and Efficiency. R. G. Hopkinson. (Paper read at the Building Research Congress 1951 and published in Division 3, Part 3 of the Congress's set of papers obtainable from the Building Research Station.)

Code for the Lighting of Building Interiors. (Illuminating Engineering Society, London.)

Colour in School Buildings. (Ministry of Education Building Bulletin No. 9, H.M.S.O., 1953.)

Computation and Measurement of Sky and Daylight Factors. P. Petherbridge. (Division 3, Part 3 of the 1951 Congress's set of papers, obtainable from the Building Research Station.)

Daylight (dwellings and schools). (British Standard Code of Practice, CP 3, Chapter I (A), 1949.)

Daylight Factor Protractors. Building Research Station. (Obtainable only direct from H.M.S.O.)

The Daylighting of Classrooms under the New Regulations. W. A. Allen and J. B. Bickerdike. (Journal of the R.I.B.A., September, 1946.)

The Daylighting of Factories. J. B. Bickerdike. (Journal of the R.I.B.A., September, 1948.)

The Development of the Use of Colour in British Factories. H. L. Gloag. (Division 3, Part 3 of the 1951 Congress's set of papers, obtainable from the Building Research Station.)

The Economics of Classroom Lighting. F. J. Farmer. (Architects' Journal, August 10, 1950.)

Factory Lighting in Great Britain. W. A. Allen and J. B. Collins. (Division 3, Part 3 of the 1951 Congress's set of papers, obtainable from the Building Research Station.)

The Factories (Standards of Lighting) Regulations (1941). S.R. & O., 1941, No. 94 (H.M.S.O.)

Fluorescent Lighting. C. Zwikker, editor. (Published by Phillip's Technical Library.)

Glare and Lighting. R. G. Hopkinson. (Architects' Journal, March 9, 1950.)

Illumination, current edition of *Specification*. W. A. Allen. (Published annually by the Architectural Press.)

Illumination Design for Interiors. (Issued by the Lighting Service Bureau, 2 Savoy Hill, London, W.C.2. Contains basic information and formulae for illumination design.)

The Influence of Daylighting Research on the Design and Layout of Buildings. W. A. Allen and J. B. Bickerdike. (Division 3, Part 3 of the 1951 Congress's set of papers, obtainable from the Building Research Station.)

Light Fittings. D. Dewar Mills. (Architectural Review, November, 1952.)

Lighting and Child Development. D. B. Harmon. (Illuminating Engineering, Vol. XL, p. 199, April, 1945 (American).)

Lighting in Industry. J. B. Bickerdike. (In book of R.I.B.A. Industrial Conference, March, 1949.)

Lighting in Industry No. 2. British Electrical Development Association. (In the Electricity Productivity series.)

Lighting in the Design of Schools. A. Pott. (Trans. of the Illuminating Engineering Society, London, Vol. XVII, No. 10, 1952.)

The Lighting of Birmingham Art Gallery. (Architects' Journal, June 8, 1950.)

The Lighting of Buildings. W. A. Allen and R. G. Hopkinson. (Journal of the R.I.B.A., April and May, 1951.)

The Lighting of Buildings. (Post-War Building Studies, No. 12, 1944.)

The Lighting of Galleries and Museums. J. B. Bickerdike and W. A. Allen. (Commission International D'Eclairage, Stockholm 1951, collected papers published 1952.)

64

The Lighting of Large Top-Lighted Picture Galleries. (The Architect and Building News, April 23, 1948. Describes proposals for the National Gallery, London.)

The Lighting of Office Buildings. (Post-War Building Studies, No. 30, 1952. H.M.S.O.)

Modern American Factories. W. A. Allen. (Journal of the R.I.B.A., February, 1953.)

Natural Lighting in Factories. W. A. Allen. (Journal of the R.I.B.A., October, 1949.)

The Natural Lighting of Houses and Flats with Graded Daylight Factor Tables. T. Smith and E. D. Brown. (D.S.I.R., H.M.S.O., 1944.)

Productivity in British Industry, No. III: High Productivity and Production Costs. Sir Claude Gibb and Gordon Baker. (The Engineer, CLXXXIX. No. 4, 912, pp. 319–322, March 17, 1950.)

Protractors for the Computation of Daylight Factors. A. F. Dufton. (D.S.I.R. Building Research Technical Paper No. 28, H.M.S.O., 1946. A new B.R.S. bulletin on the use of the Protractors is pending.)

Recent Developments in Light Sources. J. B. Bickerdike. (Architects' Journal, July 3, 1952.)

The Relation between Illumination and Industrial Efficiency. I. The Effect of Size of Work. H. C. Weston. (Joint Report of Ind. Health Res. Comm. and Illum. Res. Comm. London, H.M.S.O., 1935.)

The Relation between Illumination and Visual Efficiency. The Effect of Brightness Contrast. (Report No. 87, Ind. Health Res. Board, Med. Res. Coun., London, H.M.S.O., 1945.)

Research by the Nuffield Investigation into the Functions and Design of Hospitals. R. Llewelyn Davies. (Division 3, Part 3 of the 1951 Congress's set of papers, obtainable from the Building Research Station.)

Seasonal Variation of Daylight Illumination. Illumination Research: Technical Paper No. 17. Department of Scientific and Industrial Research. (H.M.S.O., 1935.)

Selection of Suitable Chalk Board Colours. R. G. Hopkinson. (Journal of the R.I.B.A., August, 1952.)

Sight, Light and Efficiency. H. C. Weston. (Published by H. K. Lewis, London, 1949.)

Sources and Surfaces. J. B. Bickerdike. (Architectural Review, July, 1953.)

Standards and Quality of Lighting in Schools. W. A. Allen. (Journal of the R.I.B.A., November, 1947.)

A Study of Hospital Lighting by Natural Daylighting. R. G. Hopkinson, J. Longmore and D. J. Petty. (Division 3, Part 3 of the 1951 Congress's set of papers, obtainable from the Building Research Station.)

Studies in Interior Lighting. J. M. Waldram. (Trans. of the Illuminating Engineering Society, London, Vol. XIX, No. 4, 1954.)

The Use of Louvres in Buildings. J. B. Bickerdike. (Architects' Journal, December 14, 1951.)

Window into Wall. D. Dex Harrison. (Architectural Review, August, 1950.)

HEATING OF LARGER BUILDINGS

J. R. Kell

1. INTRODUCTION

Many of the ways of heating buildings practised as the most modern to-day, are not new at all. Floor warming was used by the Romans, and yet has of recent years come to be looked on as a most advanced system, particularly in the United States. Similarly high-pressure hot water is regarded as one of the most up-to-date methods of conveying heat; yet Perkins invented the idea and put it into practice, though in a different form, over one hundred years ago. Much heating equipment available to-day is the same in principle as something made years ago. This is inevitable for principles do not change: only their application changes.

What has taken place is a steady advance in the theoretical approach to heating as a result of which systems can be designed and calculated for heating all kinds and sizes of buildings with a reasonable hope that they will achieve the temperatures specified. In the past the approach was largely empirical and frequently brought disaster when an unusual problem arose.

Then there is the widespread availability of electricity. This has enabled circulating pumps to be used on all and sundry heating systems, much to their advantage. Also the electric motor has come to be used more and more to drive fans for ventilating and for increasing the output from heating equipment as in the case of the unit heater or forced convector, of which more later. It has enabled much bigger outputs to be obtained in a given space.

Lastly, there have been many and obvious advances in appliances and techniques, owing to improved manufacturing methods, better design, the use of welding, knowledge of metallurgy, as well as general experience in the industry.

One ought not, therefore, to be discouraged by the melancholy aphorism that 'there is nothing new under the sun', but to turn to the many and great improvements and achievements which have undoubtedly been made in recent years in this field of engineering.

In the sections that follow it is proposed to touch on a few principles first, and then to discuss current methods of application.

2. GENERAL PRINCIPLES

The human body is constantly losing heat to its surroundings; if it cannot do so life becomes extinct. Heat is given out, either as sensible heat or as evaporation of moisture from the skin. If the surroundings are cool, sensible heat is given out at a greater rate than if warm, and we say we are cold. If the air is too dry, evaporation from the skin takes place at a faster rate than normal, and again we say we are cold even though the air temperature may be warm. Again, if the air moves too fast over the skin both sensible heat and moisture are given up too rapidly and we describe it as a cold draught.

Thus all three factors come into play in considering what is a state of comfort; but there is a fourth, namely radiation. Radiant heat warms directly, and the body can be comfortable in a lowish air temperature if a certain quantity of heat radiation is falling upon it.

Attempts have been made to combine all these factors into one scale: there is the Effective Temperature Scale, which combines air temperature, humidity and motion; and the Equivalent Temperature Scale, which combines air temperature and radiation. These scales require trained scientists to measure and interpret and there is as yet no one single instrument which can measure the conditions in a single reading.

The ordinary glass thermometer hung up in a room measures air temperature only, but if there is radiant heat present it will have no effect on the readings.

A globe thermometer consists of a blackened bulb in which an ordinary thermometer is fixed. Radiant heat falling on the bulb will cause the air inside the bulb to become warmer and the temperature read off will give some measure of the radiation effect. But this instrument takes no account of air motion.

The other various instruments which have been evolved need not be considered here since as stated they are not of readily practical value. The position is that the ordinary thermometer is still regarded as the criterion of a state of comfort, and in specifying the requirements for a building, temperatures in degrees Fahrenheit are as a rule alone given.

Though this, as will be apparent, is only a rough guide to comfort, it is not so far from the mark as might at first be thought, since air motion in rooms is generally slight, and humidity in this country is generally high. Also the body does not notice even wide changes in moisture content of the air. Thus apart from the effect of radiation, air temperature is a fairly reliable index of comfort.

In the heating of buildings, we therefore start with the assumption that a certain air temperature must be maintained inside, usually varying between 50 and 70°F. according to use, whilst the outside we assume is at some basic temperature such as 30 or 32°F. We also assume that conditions are steady, which, of course, they never are.

With this temperature difference between inside and outside of, say, 30–65°, i.e. 35°, heat tends to flow outwards by virtue of the conduction of heat through solid materials such as walls, windows, floors and roof. The better the conductor

67

the more rapid the loss of heat. Glass is thin and a relatively good conductor, and accounts sometimes for as much as half the losses from a building, so that it is desirable to limit its area if heat is to be saved. Concrete is a better conductor than brickwork. Air is a bad conductor of heat and hence porous materials are usually poor conductors, and are then described as insulators. By introducing an air gap into a wall the overall transmittance of heat is much reduced.

In view of the outstanding need for fuel economy owing to the fact that coal is a dwindling national asset, and also in view of the high cost of fuel in whatever form, it is clear that all new construction should be considered as much in regard to its thermal properties as any other. The addition of suitable insulation to a structure can often be shown to pay for itself in fuel savings in three to four years, and apart from this, a building which is easy to warm in winter also keeps cool in summer.

The heat lost from a building through the structure or fabric can be calculated fairly accurately from a knowledge of the temperature difference, the areas of each kind of material, its thickness, and the corresponding transmittance factor 'U', which last is explained later.

The heat losses must also include an allowance to cover the warmth carried away by natural air change such as occurs through cracks around windows and doors, up flues and so on. Even walls themselves are not impervious to air flow. Escaping warmed air is, of course, replaced by cool outside air, and the rate of air change is most difficult to assess. It is affected by wind, exposure, kind of windows and doors, air-tightness of roof where of sheeted type and so on.

There are several approaches to the estimation of air change rate, but probably at present the simplest is to select one of the accepted standards set down in the Institution of Heating and Ventilating Engineers' publications. This latter also gives temperatures usually adopted, as well as transmittance values for various materials, insulation factors, exposure and height factors and other information.

The natural air change or infiltration of a building is often much more than is required for good ventilation, and as it may represent about one-third of the total heat losses, it is well worth spending money to reduce it. Weatherstripping of windows cuts down the overall losses sometimes by one-tenth. Leakages from sheeted buildings can also readily be stopped. In one way or another the building designer should strive to cut down chance air change to a minimum: by so doing he will be saving fuel for all time.

It will be apparent from the above that the form of the building itself determines the quantity of heat required to maintain a comfortable temperature inside. The construction of the building also affects the heating problem in another way. A building may be regarded as a thermal reservoir. A massively constructed building will have a large reservoir effect, whereas a lightly constructed building will not. With variation of external temperature, the heat stored in a heavily constructed building will even out the variations so that the heating system may contribute heat at a fairly steady rate and maintain a constant internal temperature more or less regardless of the daily fluctuations of temperature outside. This would not be the case, however, with a lightly constructed building having a small thermal storage effect, and in this case the heat input would have to be varied over wide limits according to the variations of the outside temperature, in order to maintain a constant internal temperature.

A good deal of research work is being done on the thermal characteristics of buildings, and on the response rate of various forms of construction and linings of rooms, and no doubt a good deal more attention will in future be given to this aspect of heating engineering than has been given in the past.

Before proceeding further, it would be as well to explain one or two terms commonly used:

The British Thermal Unit or B.T.U. is a unit quantity of heat equal to that absorbed by 1 lb. of water when raised through 1° Fahrenheit.

The Transmittance Factor 'U', is the overall coefficient of heat transfer through building construction and is given in B.T.U.s per hour per square foot per degree difference F. For instance, the 'U' value for a $13\frac{1}{2}$-in. brick wall plastered is about 0.27; for a single glazed window 1.0; for an asbestos-cement corrugated roof 1.4, and for the latter lined with insulating board 0.31.

Specific Heat is a measure of the quantity of heat which can be stored in a certain mass of substance, and is related to the specific heat of water which is 1.0. Specific heats of building materials are, for instance, concrete, brick, plaster, etc. about 0.2; timber 0.5. The quantity of heat stored in 100 lb. of brickwork between the temperatures of 50 and 60°F. would therefore be $100 \times 10 \times 0.2 =$ 200 B.T.U.s The specific heat of air may be taken as .019 B.T.U.s per cu. ft. at the temperatures used in air change calculations.

Expansion. All common materials expand on heating. The coefficient of linear expansion per degree F. is, approximately:

.0000063 for mild steel   .0000012 for brickwork

.0000055 for concrete   .000036   for water (at 60°F.)

Latent Heat. When water is heated its temperature will steadily rise to the boiling point of 212°F. at atmospheric pressure. If the vessel is open and heat continues to be added the temperature will rise no further but steam will be formed and driven off from the surface. Each 1 lb. of water evaporated will contain a quantity of heat termed the latent heat, equal to approximately 970 B.T.U.s per lb. If the steam is condensed on a cool surface the latent heat will be given up and will cause the cooler body or fluid to be warmed, this being the mechanism of heat transmission by steam. If the steam and water are in a closed vessel and heat continues to be applied, the pressure of the steam will rise and the temperature will rise also above atmospheric boiling point.

3. PRODUCTION OF HEAT

In order to gain a general picture of the heating problem it is necessary now to envisage as above described first the building continually giving up heat to the outside air, and this heat of necessity being replaced inside to maintain a steady temperature; we then have to consider means of producing this artificial heat in the various rooms. One way is to provide a fire in each room but the burning of fuel requires labour to carry it to the various points required, also numerous flues have to be got away through the roof and the heat so obtained is fluctuating. It is not a method which can be regarded seriously for the heating of large buildings, and we therefore turn to the production of heat outside the rooms to be heated and its conveyance to the inside through some form of heat-conveying medium. Such a system is termed Central Heating, but it may be applied on a much bigger scale whereby a number of buildings are heated from one main source, and the system is then described as District Heating.

The production of heat necessitates combustion of fuel in a device which can absorb the heat and transfer it to the conveying medium. This device is the boiler and the fuel may be either coal, coke, oil or gas. Electricity may also similarly be used to heat a transmitting medium outside the rooms to be heated.

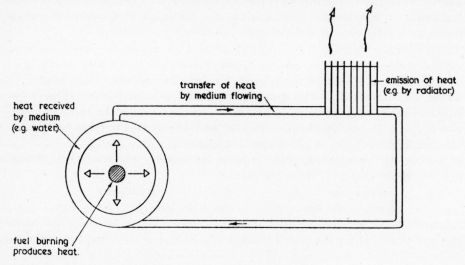

51. *Diagram of heat transfer from fuel to room in a central heating system.*

4. CONVEYING OF HEAT

The conveying medium in a Central Heating System is commonly water or steam, although other liquids or air may also be used.

Water is most commonly used in Great Britain on account of the ease with which the temperature may be varied to suit changing atmospheric temperature. The water is heated at one point and circulated through a system of pipes to the rooms required to be heated, in which are contained the heat-emitting elements. The circulation consists of a flow pipe from the boiler to the emitter, and a return pipe back to the boiler in a closed circuit. If the element is at a level above the boiler this circulation can be by gravity or thermo syphon, which operates because water expands on heating and therefore the rising column from the boiler is less in density than the cooler falling column from the heating element back to the boiler. The size of installation in which gravity circulation may be used economically is limited because the circulating forces are small and hence large pipes are required. It is now usual on all but the smallest installations to accelerate the circulation by means of a centrifugal pump, usually electrically driven. The circulation in a system containing such a pump is thus independent of the temperature of the water, the pipes can be kept smaller in size, and more rapid heating up will be possible.

A low-pressure hot water system is one using water at a temperature usually up to 180°F. at the boiler, and such a system is usually open to atmosphere by means of a tank which keeps the system filled.

If the tank is replaced by a closed vessel in which an air or steam cushion is maintained under pressure, the temperature of the water can be raised above atmospheric boiling point and at about 250°F. would be termed a Medium-Pressure System, and at about 300°F. and over a High-Pressure Hot Water System. The pressure necessary to be maintained at 250°F. would be about 15 lb. per square inch and at 300°F. about 50 lb. per square inch.

It is usual to use low-pressure hot water for small and medium-sized installations up to a total of 3 to 5 million B.T.U.s per hour; and above this to consider either medium- or high-pressure hot water, or steam. The reason for choice of one system as against another may be briefly referred to as follows:

Low-Pressure Hot Water: A given quantity of water in circulation can carry only a small amount of heat owing to the limitation of temperature drop, e.g. boiler flow 180°F., return 150°F.=30° drop, or 30 B.T.U.s per lb. of water circulating.

Medium- and High-Pressure Hot Water: These are more suitable for conveying large quantities of heat over long distances. The water in circulation if at 300°F. flow and 200°F. return=100° drop will carry 100 B.T.U.s per lb. Smaller pipes may therefore be used than with a low-pressure hot water system. Also the heat-emitting elements will be smaller owing to the higher temperature of the surfaces.

Steam: Steam suffers from the disadvantage of not being so flexible, as to temperature variation to suit weather, as is hot water. Steam, in effect, must be on or off, as the variation in temperature with pressure is relatively small as will be seen from reference to a table of the properties of steam. Steam is, however, widely used in industry for process work and other purposes, and has long been a favourite as a means of heating in individual buildings because of its cheapness and simplicity. One pound of steam carries the latent heat of nearly

1,000 B.T.U.s and the size of pipes required is generally less than with hot water excepting in the larger sizes of high-pressure hot water installations, such as say 10 million B.T.U.s per hr. and over.

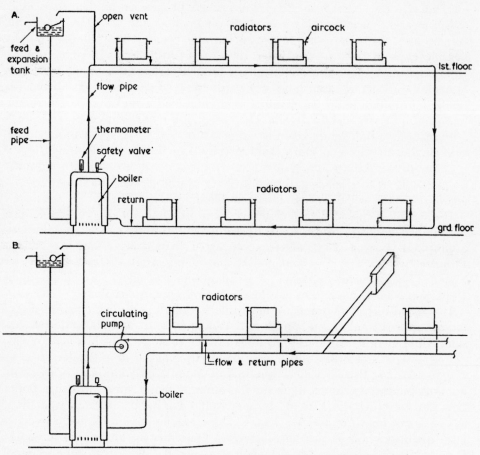

52. *Diagrams of low-pressure hot water systems:* (a) *gravity circulation;* (b) *pump circulation.*

The steam when condensed in the heat-emitting elements can either be run to waste, which is extravagant in fuel and water, or it can be returned through a system of condense return pipes back to the boiler for re-evaporation. To prevent steam passing direct into the condense return pipes, a steam trap is commonly used at each outlet, and in large installations there may be many hundreds of such traps. A certain amount of air and other gases are carried with the steam, and sometimes condensed water is corrosive to iron piping so that other materials such as copper are often used.

5. EMISSION OF HEAT

The mechanism by which heat is given off from a heated body or surface in a room is simple in comparison with the wide variety of methods and types of apparatus now developed for this purpose.

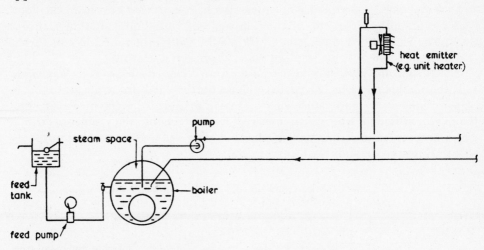

53. *Diagram of a high-pressure hot water system.*

A heated body will give out heat to surrounding space by one (or more) of three means:

(1) First by *Convection* – that is by the warming of the air immediately in contact with the hot surface. The air expands, becomes less dense, and hence rises, being replaced by cooler air which in turn becomes heated, rises and so on. In a room a circulation is set up, warm air rising from the heat emitter, passing across the ceiling and falling to the floor after coming in contact with the cooler walls, windows, etc. From the floor it returns to the heated surface where the cycle is repeated. The currents so set up are described as convection currents. The hotter the surface of the emitter the more rapid will be the circulation, and the greater the difference of temperature between the ceiling and floor.

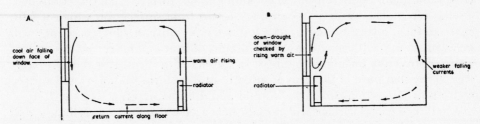

54. *Diagram of convection currents in a room heated by radiator or convector:* (*a*) *on inner wall,* (*b*) *under window.*

73

This difference is termed the temperature gradient and is recognized as having an important effect in the selection of the temperature of operation of the heating surfaces as well as of their location with regard to the positions of the cooling surfaces.

An unfortunate consequence of convection heating is that dust from the floor is picked up in the airstream, becomes heated and causes dirty markings on the walls. The higher the temperature of the air the more pronounced is this effect, and it is one of the reasons why hot water is preferred to steam.

(2) The second method of heat transfer from a heated surface is by *Radiation*. It is the method by which heat is received on the earth from the sun, and is akin to light waves and radio waves. Heat radiation is longer in wavelength than light, although 'white' heat and 'red' heat merge into the visible spectrum. At lower temperatures the wavelengths are longer still and for heating purposes we are concerned mainly with this region.

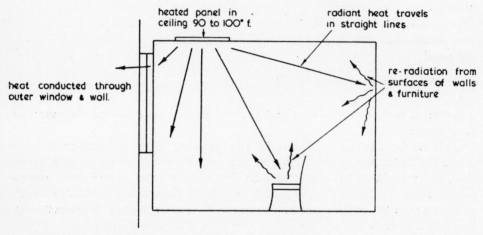

55. *Diagram of heat emission in a room by radiation.*

All radiation travels in straight lines at a speed of 186,000 miles per second. Heat radiation is emitted from every point of a hot surface in all directions over a semi-sphere. Heat radiation can be reflected from surfaces on which it falls, or it can be absorbed by bodies at a lower temperature in which case they will be warmed and will become in turn radiators of heat at a longer wavelength as well as convectors warming up the air in contact with them. It is thus probably true to say that most of the heat emitted in radiant form from a heated surface ends up in convection currents of a mild and diffused nature.

A polished metal surface will radiate heat less and reflect more than a dull black one. As to whether a surface is black, white, or some other colour, is unimportant at the range of wavelengths in which we are mainly interested.

74

A human body in a room having a radiant heat source is warmed by the direct rays of heat and this is generally agreed as a pleasanter form of providing comfort than that of relying on heated air. Radiant systems are thus tending to become more generally used.

A radiant system will also produce some convection currents from the heated surfaces, but where these are overhead the tendency to soiling of decorations is less evident, particularly with surfaces at low temperatures.

(3) The third method of heat transfer, namely, *Conduction* concerns the carrying of heat through the solid mass of a body and although it enters indirectly into most applications of heating, it does not arise in the present context.

6. CONVECTIVE AND RADIANT SYSTEMS

It will be apparent from the foregoing that the two methods of emitting heat in rooms may be classified under the headings 'mainly convective' and 'mainly radiant'. Mainly convective systems are those which rely chiefly on the warming of air for the conveying of heat about the room. Mainly radiant systems are those which make use of heated surfaces to transmit heat by radiation.

It will also be evident that a second classification may be made according to temperature. Convection elements may be heated by steam or hot water to any temperature from about 150°F. to 300°F., but the air heated indirectly may range from about 90 to 200°F.

If heated to too high a temperature air becomes parched and stuffy, and hence the use of bigger volumes at lower temperatures is desirable. Also the higher the temperature of air discharged from a convector, the more buoyant it is, and the greater its tendency to rise sharply to the ceiling, consequently

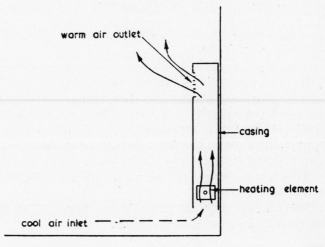

warm air outlet

casing

heating element

cool air inlet

56. Section of a convector.

75

with greater heat losses by transmission and leakage at the upper levels. Probably about 120° is a desirable maximum temperature for the air issuing from a convector.

Considering the classification of 'mainly radiant' systems according to temperature, we can use very large areas of floors heated by embedded hot water coils, or by electric resistance wires, to about 75°F. at the surface, or heated ceilings at about 100°F. Such systems are known as panel heating. At the other end of the scale, we can have small luminous elements electrically or gas heated at about 2,500°F. Between these limits in common use, we have metal-faced panels using hot water at low pressure at about 160°F. mean, giving a surface temperature of perhaps 140°F. and the recently developed high-temperature metal panels heated by steam or hot water, to about 300°F.

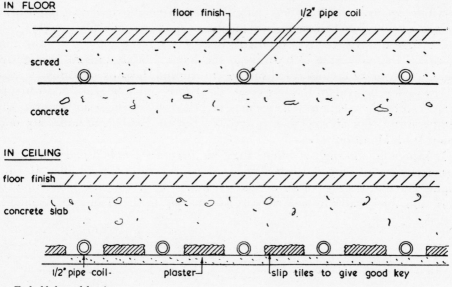

IN FLOOR

floor finish⌐   1/2" pipe coil

screed

concrete

IN CEILING

floor finish

concrete slab

1/2" pipe coil⌐   plaster⌐   ⌐slip tiles to give good key

57. *Embedded panel heating.*

It is a characteristic of radiant systems that the air is heated only secondarily, thus it is at a lower temperature than with a convective system; losses are usually less, and consequently less heat suffices to maintain a given comfort level with resulting fuel economy. It is also a characteristic of radiant heating that temperatures are very uniform throughout the heated space, because of the wide dispersal and reflection of the radiation already referred to.

To return to convection systems, a further sub-division needs to be considered, *natural* and *forced*.

Natural convectors are those already described which rely on the natural air currents set up from heated elements.

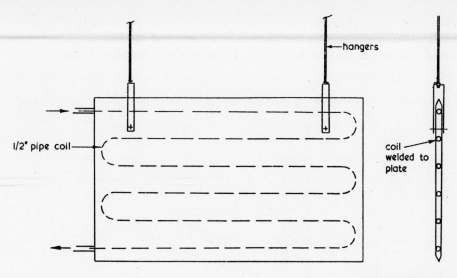

hangers

1/2" pipe coil

coil welded to plate

showing double-sided type

58. *High-temperature metal panels.*

Forced convectors are those in which the air current is generated by an electric fan. By this means a much greater output can be obtained from a given area of finned tubular element with obvious economy and wider range of application. Unit heaters are a well-known method of heating large spaces and come under the category of forced convectors. By good design and selection of unit heaters, fairly uniform heating may be obtained in large space heating, but a bad installation may produce patchy results with marked temperature gradients.

Developments on the lines of the unit heater have produced of recent years

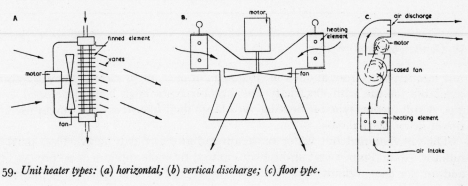

59. *Unit heater types: (a) horizontal; (b) vertical discharge; (c) floor type.*

the classroom type of heater which is, in effect, a unit of special type with slow-speed silent fan applicable to the heating of schools and the like.

Forced convectors may be heated by hot water with pumped circulation at

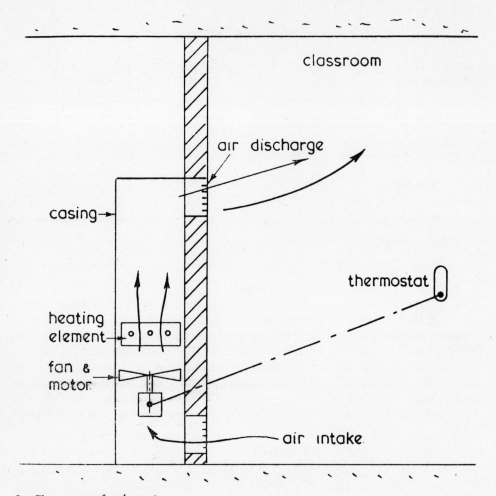

60. *Classroom-type forced convector.*

any temperatures from about 180° to 300°F. or over, or by steam. They are also available for use with electricity and certain types have been developed for gas. A still further type for heating very large shed-like structures makes use of direct firing by coal, coke or oil.

The conventional hot water or steam radiator is partly convective, partly radiant. About 80 per cent of the heat emitted by such appliances is convective and 20 per cent radiant, and hence the term 'radiator' is really a misnomer.

Exposed pipe coils are in a similar category, as also are electric tubular heaters. Hot water radiators usually operate at a mean temperature of about 160°F.; with steam the temperature may be about 220°F.; the higher the temperature the smaller is the surface needed, but the greater is the tendency to charring of dust particles. This latter is no doubt the cause of the complaints about central heating producing a stuffy atmosphere and it suggests that high-temperature surfaces should be avoided, particularly with convective systems.

An interesting system employing a mixture of radiation and convection is the Baseboard Heater which appears to have originated in America. In this sytem a metal skirting is used, behind which are heating elements which serve to heat the surface and at the same time to warm air which rises through apertures provided at top and bottom for the purpose. The warmed currents rise along the full length of the walls and are thus very uniformly distributed.

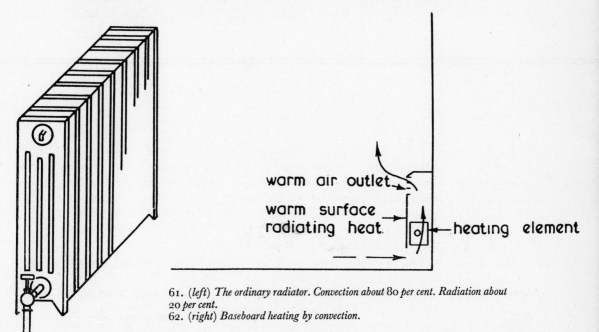

61. (*left*) *The ordinary radiator. Convection about* 80 *per cent. Radiation about* 20 *per cent.*
62. (*right*) *Baseboard heating by convection.*

What is probably the latest invention in the form of heat emitters is a ceiling panel system known as Frenger, of Continental origin. This consists of a series of perforated painted metal plates, two feet square, forming the ceiling, clipped up to a grid of pipes which are heated with hot water to about 160° to 180°F. The upper surface of the plates is insulated with glass silk and the purpose is to combine heating with acoustical treatment. The plates are of small heat capacity and hence very responsive to control. The latter remark serves to introduce the consideration of the time-lag of a heating system.

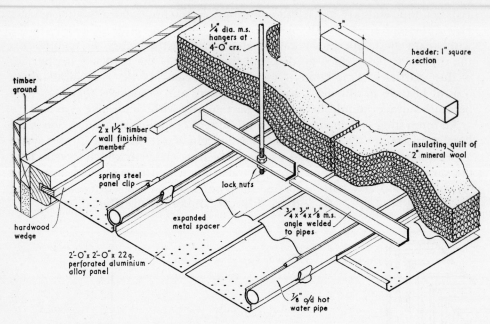

63. *The Frenger system of ceiling panel heating.*

Any apparatus of a convective nature is usually of small heat capacity and hence can be adjusted rapidly either by hand or thermostatically to suit changing weather conditions or occupancy. On the other hand an embedded panel system which makes use of the warming of the structure of floors or ceilings for the heating surfaces must have a long time-lag, which in buildings having a considerable variation of conditions may be a disadvantage. In other cases the steady output of heat may be an advantage.

Hot water systems generally have a longer time-lag than steam systems because of the heat stored in the circulating fluid.

The selection of the type of system best suited for any particular building is therefore a complicated one, deriving from a weighing up of the considerations briefly touched on above as well as of the economics of first cost and running cost.

The next section is an attempt to give some examples of possible alternative methods of heating buildings of various kinds, with the reasons affecting choice.

7. HEATING OF BUILDING TYPES
Factories
Large single-storey shed-type factories. These usually present a big heating load, and here low temperature systems such as ordinary pipes and radiators become

uneconomical. Methods can be summarized as follows:

(*a*) Unit heaters heated by steam or high-temperature hot water are commonly adopted and if well designed and positioned, can be quite successful. Unit heaters are of three main types: horizontal blow type for mounting on columns on side walls about 10 ft. from floor; vertical discharge type for fixing at roof-truss level; and floor mounting type, which draw in air near floor and discharge at high level overhead. The selection of the most suitable type and the mounting positions, length of blow and air volumes handled, needs careful consideration in design.

(*b*) High-temperature metal panels are being increasingly used for this type of building and have many advantages, as already discussed. There are no moving parts and no maintenance. They are usually mounted between columns down the length of a shop about 10–14 ft. above the floor, or sloping or horizontally under the roof. These panels are fed with either steam or high-temperature hot water (Fig. 72).

(*c*) The plenum system is in effect a ventilating system in which the air is raised to sufficient temperature to warm the building. Large ducts are involved and even distribution of heat is not easy to achieve; as a result it has fallen into disfavour except in special cases.

(*d*) Floor warming by embedded panels is being practised extensively in America, but has the disadvantage in factory work of a tendency to warming of the feet, which some consider unpleasant; also machine beds cannot be arranged for with impunity.

Small factories or workshops, and multi-storey factory buildings. For these the following are generally suitable according to size: hot water pipes and radiators, steam or hot water convectors (natural or forced), overhead metal panels at mean temperatures of about 160°F. or less.

Factory buildings of this type often have a large heat gain from machinery, motors, process plant and occupants, and this is often almost sufficient to keep the building warm once it has been raised to temperature. A system which is rapidly responsive to control is desirable and for this reason embedded panel heating is not to be recommended for such buildings.

Office Blocks

(*a*) Pipes and radiators using low-pressure hot water are a common and economical system, though they take up space and are liable to cause wall markings as referred to.

(*b*) Metal panels heated by low-pressure hot water may be used as an alternative to radiators under windows to give improved appearance.

(*c*) Convectors: These may be built in and give a cleaner appearance than radiators. Being purely convective they are considered by some to produce the warmed-air effect mentioned previously. (Fig. 74.)

(*d*) Embedded ceiling panels – many of the largest buildings have this system installed with very satisfactory results. The temperature throughout such buildings is markedly uniform; the absence of convection currents results in clean decorations over long periods and there is a complete freedom of architectural treatment because there are no obstructions on the floor or walls.

(*e*) The Frenger ceiling panel system – combining acoustical treatment with heating is well worth consideration. It has the advantage of (*d*) without the disadvantage of a long time-lag.

Hospitals

(*a*) Radiators of hospital type (i.e. with easily cleaned surfaces) are frequently adopted and are satisfactory.

(*b*) Embedded panel system – this is particularly suitable for hospitals owing to its inherent cleanliness, if the extra cost over radiators is acceptable.

(*c*) Convectors do not appear so suitable in hospitals owing to the hidden spaces in the enclosures which are not readily cleanable. Air-conditioning would be appropriate in certain departments (see later).

Schools

The following methods are all applicable, and comparisons of cost and individual preference will usually dictate the choice: (*a*) Pipes and radiators. (*b*) Natural convectors. (*c*) Classroom-type forced convectors. (*d*) Embedded floor panel (Fig. 86). (*e*) Embedded ceiling panel. (*f*) Baseboard heating.

Churches

(*a*) Pipes and radiators are generally adopted for economy and simplicity.

(*b*) Natural or forced classroom convectors would be applicable in some churches.

(*c*) Floor panel heating supplemented by radiators under large windows, particularly those at high level.

(*d*) Electrically heated panels in pews or electric tubular heaters.

Theatres and Cinemas

A ventilating system is usually required by regulation and the heating is then confined to dealing with the fabric losses of the auditorium, plus normal heating of dressing rooms, entrances, and so on.

A low-pressure hot water system using radiators or natural convectors is usually most suitable.

Alternatively, full air-conditioning may be adopted, giving the advantage of controlled temperatures and humidities both in summer and winter.

Farm Buildings

For animal sheds, embedded floor warming at low temperature or, alternatively, overhead metal panels are suitable.

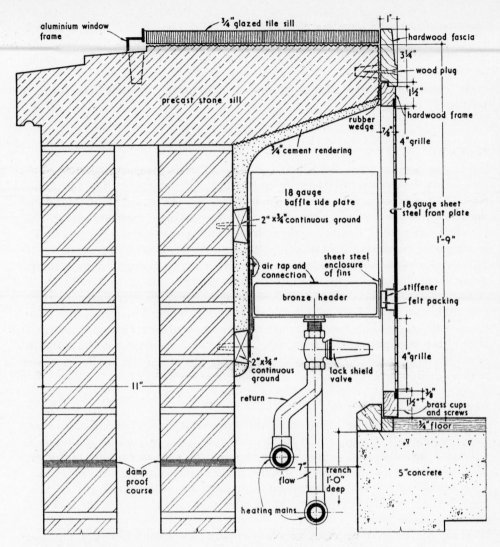

64. *Section through a window sill in the assembly hall of a Leeds school (Architect: R. A. H. Livett), showing a typical heating convector.*

Colleges

Lecture rooms: Embedded ceiling panels; pipes and radiators, or convectors, natural or forced.

Laboratories: Here there is often a big build-up of heat from bunsen burners and so on, when apparatus is in use, and a quick response to control is desirable. Suitable systems are: Frenger ceiling panel; forced or natural convectors; pipes and radiators.

Here quick response to control is desirable to suit variations in occupancy. Suitable systems are: convectors, natural or forced; Frenger ceiling panels; metal panels.

Air conditioning may also be regarded as desirable in the larger stores if financially possible.

8. FUEL

There has been a quiet revolution taking place over the past 25 years or so, greatly accelerated by the War, in the matter of boiler plants. The old stoke-hole was a dark and dirty pit in which it was known that down below there lurked some low-paid individual who 'did the stoking'. Fuel was cheap and plentiful and no one worried much so long as there was plenty of steam or hot water when required. To-day boiler houses can be as clean as the kitchen. Labour consists only of a white-coated attendant who looks in for a few minutes a day to see that all is running correctly. Automatic controls do the rest.

The reasons for this dramatic change are not far to seek. They are: (*a*) High cost and scarcity of fuel which impels building owners to install the most efficient plant. (*b*) High cost of labour and scarcity of stokers; consequently automatic burning equipment is required. (*c*) A general appreciation that cleanliness and daylight, giving better working conditions, make for economy in maintenance and improved operation in the long run.

Choice of Fuel

The kinds of fuel commonly available in this country, are coal, coke, oil, gas, and electricity. The selection of the kind of fuel for a new building project is dependent usually on: (*a*) comparative running cost; (*b*) availability of supply; (*c*) value placed on amenities such as cleanliness and convenience.

Comparative running costs can be estimated; for instance, the cost of heat from *coal* can be calculated from a knowledge of calorific value of the fuel and efficiency of the boiler.

Assuming the calorific value at 12,000 British Thermal Units (B.T.U.s) per pound, and working boiler efficiency at 70 per cent, we have in 1 ton

$$2,240 \times 12,000 \times \frac{70}{100} = 18,800,000 \text{ B.T.U.s}$$

or converting to therms (1 therm = 100,000 B.T.U.s)
$$= 188 \text{ therms per ton.}$$

If coal costs 80*s*. per ton, the cost of producing

$$1 \text{ therm} = \frac{80 \times 12}{188}$$
$$= 5.1d./\text{therm.}$$

Oil is usually priced in pence per gallon; here we might have for example:

Calorific value   18,500 B.T.U.s/lb.

Specific gravity   .9

Efficiency of boiler 75 per cent

$$10 \text{ lb./gal.} \times .9 \times 18,500 \times \frac{75}{100} = 125,000$$
$$= 1.25 \text{ therms.}$$

cost of oil, say 1/- per gallon,

$$\text{cost per therm} = \frac{12}{1.25}$$
$$= 9.6d./\text{therm.}$$

Gas is charged on a therm basis, but this is for the heat in the gas supplied. The heat actually available from the boiler depends again on the boiler efficiency, and if this is 75 per cent, the number of therms of gas to produce

$$1 \text{ therm of heat} = \frac{1 \times 100}{75} = 1.33$$

If gas is charged at 18d./therm, cost per therm of heat output $= 18 \times 1.33$
$$= 24d./\text{therm.}$$

Electricity. 1 unit is equivalent to 3,415 B.T.U.s Efficiency of conversion is 100 per cent. If priced at 1d. per unit the cost per therm is thus

$$\frac{100,000 \times 1}{3,415} = 29.2d.$$

In order to estimate roughly the number of therms consumed per annum by a given building, we may take the cubic contents and allow an average factor of say $2\frac{1}{2}$ B.T.U.s per cu. ft. in order to arrive at the maximum heat load. The equivalent hours-use at full load per annum depends on weather, kind and times of occupancy, week-end programme, etc. If we assume however, by way of example, annual equivalent heating hours at full load $=2,000$, and a building of 1 million cu. ft., we have

$$\frac{1,000,000 \times 2.5 \times 2,000}{100,000} = 50,000 \text{ therms p.a.}$$

Comparative fuel costs are then (using the figures above):

Coal $50,000 \times$ 5.1d. – £1,060 per annum

Oil $50,000 \times$ 9.6d. – £2,000   ,,   ,,

Gas $50,000 \times 24.0d$. – £5,000   ,,   ,,

Electricity $50,000 \times 29.5d$. – £6,150   ,,   ,,

A straight comparison on cost per therm of heat as above is not necessarily correct as some fuels are more easily controlled thermostatically and hence less susceptible of waste than others. Gas, oil and electricity would score over coal in this respect.

The annual bill for heating includes, in addition to fuel, such items as labour and maintenance, which have to be taken into account in making a comparison. Obviously, here also, coal is at a disadvantage.

Sufficient has perhaps been said to indicate the lines on which a comparison can be made and the various factors which need to be taken into account in making a true comparison before final selection of the fuel to be used.

9. BOILERS

Boilers are nowadays self-contained instead of having the old-fashioned brick settings. Types available for various ranges of duty may be briefly summarized as follows:

Up to $2\frac{1}{2}$ million B.T.U.s/hr. per boiler: cast iron sectional type (Fig. 65).

1 million to 5 million B.T.U.s/hr.: steel sectional type (Fig. 66).

3 million to 15 million B.T.U.s/hr.: cylindrical Economic or Super-Economic type (Fig. 67)

5 million to 30 million B.T.U.s/hr.: water-tube, or high-velocity water-tube type (La Mont) (Fig. 68).

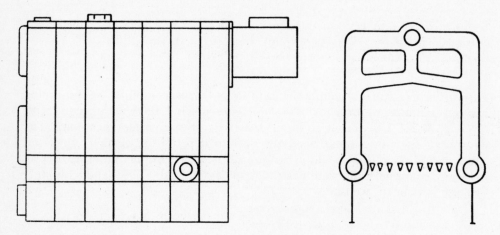

65. *Cast-iron sectional boiler.*

There are many variations and the duties named are not the limits, but a rough guide only. Cast iron and steel sectional types are used for low-pressure hot water or low-pressure steam; cylindrical and water-tube types for higher pressures of steam or hot water, though they also may be used for low pressures.

Efficiencies range from about 65 per cent for cast iron sectional type to 80 per cent or over for Super-Economic and water-tube types. Efficiency depends as much on the method of firing as on design.

86

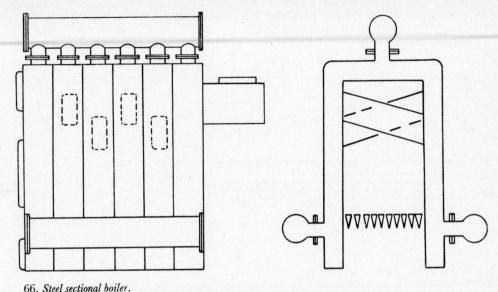

66. *Steel sectional boiler.*

In deciding on the size and number of boilers to be installed, it is always desirable to include some spare capacity as standby. In the case of a two-boiler installation, for instance, each might be designed to handle two-thirds full load. If four boilers are installed, one might be a complete standby, and might come into use in periods of exceptional cold.

Automatic firing of the fuel, combined with automatic temperature or pressure control as referred to already, is synonymous with a modern plant if this is to be run at a continuous high efficiency, with minimum of labour (Fig. 89).

For coal, automatic stokers are available, and these can be arranged to

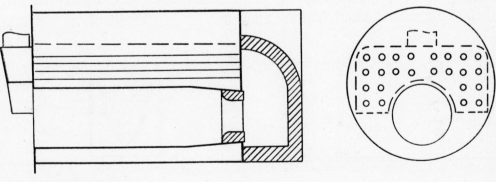

67. *Economic type boiler.*

87

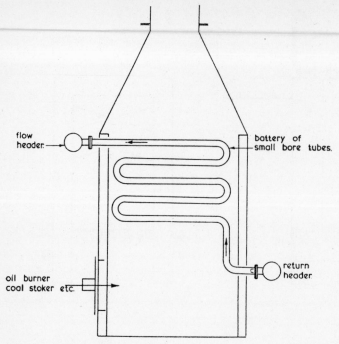

68. *La Mont boiler.*

convey the fuel direct from the bunker to the boiler. The only labour is then removing ash and clinker.

For coke or coke breeze, gravity feed boilers have been designed and although some early examples required a good deal of maintenance, these disadvantages have now been largely overcome.

For small anthracite also, gravity feed conversion units are available for certain types of boiler.

Oil firing is dealt with by fitting an oil burner to the boiler. Oil burners are of various types to suit different requirements and kinds of oil (Fig. 90). The self-contained fully automatic system meets a wide variety of needs and has much to commend it. Other systems are low-pressure air, medium-pressure air

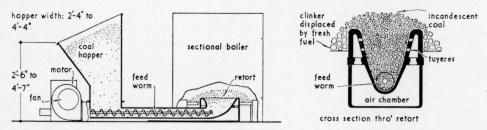

69. *Sections through a mechanical stoker (Riley Stoker Co.) of the Robot hopper type fitted to a sectional boiler.*

and pressure jet. Tankage for the oil is generally provided by means of large cylindrical or rectangular steel tanks with filling pipe from roadway.

Gas firing may be applied to almost any type of boiler, but for maximum efficiency special gas boilers are probably desirable. Up to about $1\frac{1}{2}$ million B.T.U.s/hr., these may be of cast iron, but above this, they are of steel multi-tubular type either vertical or horizontal.

Electricity, if not used direct in the rooms, is usually taken at night-time, so as to make use of cheap off-peak current. The plant then comprises electrode boilers and thermal storage cylinders, the latter being run up to a high temperature to reduce the capacity. The system of heating in the rooms is by hot water supplied through a blending valve so as to reduce the temperature of the water received from the cylinders. This system, of course, requires no flue as do the other fuels.

In the matter of cleanliness, electricity, gas and oil enable a perfectly clean boiler house to be maintained and the labour is negligible. Coal and coke involve some dust in the de-clinkering process, and possibly some dust and dirt at the discharge point of the fuel; this can, however, be limited by careful arrangement.

Where low-pressure hot water systems are to be served from steam or high-pressure hot water boilers, calorifiers or heat exchangers are used. Hot water for supplies to taps is also obtainable from similar appliances of storage type and these too may be used with low-pressure hot water in order to avoid furring of the boiler.

10. DISTRICT HEATING

Where a large number of buildings are served from one boiler house, the system is described as district heating. The boiler house may be placed at a distance, such as in an industrial area near to rail transport for coal, and where a tall chimney is not objectionable. The boiler may use a low-grade coal and means be provided for smoke and grit elimination.

Alternatively, the heat may be derived from exhaust steam from a power station, so making a highly efficient combination known as a thermo-electric station.

From the boiler house or power station, insulated main pipes conveying hot water or steam are carried in concrete ducts under roads and footpaths to serve the various buildings (Figs. 91, 92). The heating systems in the buildings are of normal type and are connected either direct to the mains or through calorifiers. Similarly, hot water supply may be catered for from the same mains.

Means of metering the heat supplied to each block of premises is included except where these are too small to warrant the expense, in which case a rental charge is made for the heat supplied.

Many large schemes exist on the Continent and in America, but in this country they are confined, so far, mainly to housing estates, some groups of flats, and a few industrial estates. One interesting system is in the Pimlico Flats scheme, London, where heat is supplied from Battersea Power Station by mains carried in a tunnel under the River Thames. A large vertical cylindrical heat accumulator is provided to balance out the variations in rate of heat supply and give a steady output to the flats.

On the face of it, it appears absurd that each building in a modern city should have its own boiler house for heating, each with its own fuel deliveries, ash disposal, labour for stoking, and flue for spreading fumes and smoke into the atmosphere we breath and live in. How much better to have no more than a pipe connection from heating mains in the street just as with water and gas.

The economic problems involved in district heating at the present time, however, are proving an insuperable barrier. The present high cost of constructional work, the restrictions on capital expenditure and the element of financial risk involved have caused many schemes which have been examined to be turned down. It was anticipated that some of the New Towns would have been so equipped, but this appears now to be unlikely.

The technical advantages of district heating are such that it is to be hoped that when conditions change at some future date, big-scale schemes will be carried out.

11. THE HEAT PUMP

Another method of producing heat is the heat pump, which has received a good deal of publicity in recent years, as it appears to give something for nothing. The possibilities were first expounded by Lord Kelvin in 1862, so again the invention cannot be described as new.

The principle of the heat pump is that of the refrigerating machine. In the normal case a refrigerating compressor compresses a gas such as ammonia or freon, the gas is cooled and condensed into a liquid in a condenser from which the heat is removed by air or water. The liquid is then expanded through a small orifice, so reducing its pressure and in this condition it will take heat from its surroundings by boiling at the low pressure. This boiling takes place in the evaporator which constitutes the cooling element or freezing coil of the refrigerator. The vapour resulting from the evaporation then passes to the compressor for recompression, and the cycle is repeated.

In the heat pump, interest centres on the condenser, the heated water from which may be used to warm a building. The evaporator is supplied with heat from any low-grade heat source, such as a river, or waste cooling water. The heat available from the condenser is equal to the sum of the heat supplied gratis from the low-grade source, plus the heat equivalent of the power applied at the compressor. Within suitable temperature limits the ratio of heat input to heat output may be as much as 3:1 or an 'efficiency' of 300 per cent.

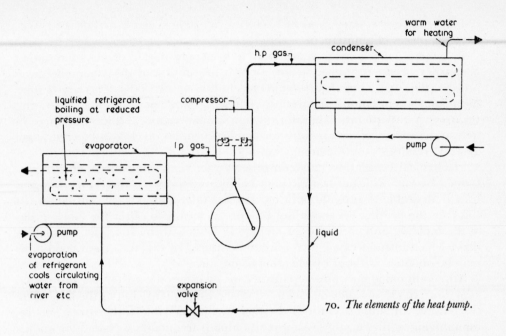

liquified refrigerant
boiling at reduced
pressure

evaporator

l p gas

compressor

h.p gas

condenser

warm water
for heating

pump

pump

evaporation
of refrigerant
cools circulating
water from
river etc

expansion
valve

liquid

70. *The elements of the heat pump.*

One snag is that the wider the temperature difference between evaporator and condenser, the less the advantage, and this limits the use to low-temperature systems. Another snag is the high cost of refrigerating plant in comparison with boiler plants of equal duty.

It appears that a definite fuel economy must result from such a system, but this also must be qualified since it has to be borne in mind that the power used to drive the compressor, if electrical, has come from a power station with a thermal efficiency of 20–25 per cent, thus a 3:1 saving at the using end is counterbalanced by a 4:1 loss at the producing end. Alternatively, an engine such as a diesel, or gas, engine may be used to drive the compressor and the waste heat from the exhaust be harnessed to add to that from the heat pump. This is the method adopted at the experimental plant at the Royal Festival Hall of the London County Council. Here again, however, the added capital cost and maintenance of the prime mover has to be allowed for.

In practice, taking all factors into account, it is found difficult to make a sound economic case for the heat pump, when compared with heat produced from fuel in a boiler, and its future would appear to be limited to a few special cases.

12. VENTILATION AND AIR-CONDITIONING

Ventilation in some form is an essential in any building. It may be furnished by merely opening windows, or by natural roof ventilation, or a mechanical system may be necessary to meet Factories Act requirements or Local Regulations for places of amusement.

In general, mechanical ventilation is necessary in all places of crowded occupancy or where fumes, steam, or heat are produced in a manufacturing process (Fig. 94). Thus theatres, cinemas and assembly halls generally require mechanical ventilation, as also do kitchens, laundries, hospital operating theatres, X-ray rooms, laboratories and similar rooms. Office buildings in industrial cities may also require mechanical ventilation, because of the noise and dirt resulting from opening windows.

Mechanical ventilation may comprise extract ventilation mechanically performed by fans with natural air inlet behind radiators or convectors, but it is usually desirable to provide both mechanical inlet and extract ventilation. In this case the heating is carried out by normal means to offset the fabric losses of the building only, and the air change is dealt with by the inlet ventilating plant which introduces air at room temperature. In this way fresh conditions may be obtained without overheating of the air.

Air-conditioning goes one step further, by enabling the air temperature to be kept down in the summer by means of refrigerating plant, and at the same time the relative humidity is controlled either by humidifying in the winter, or de-humidifying in the summer. Air-conditioning is frequently required for manufacturing processes in order to obtain steady atmospheric conditions throughout the year, on which the success of many such processes now depends. Air-conditioning for comfort only in this country is by way of being a luxury, except in special cases where long periods of crowded occupancy render conditions in summer unpleasant. In warmer climates air-conditioning is becoming general for office buildings, shops, dwellings, hospitals, factories, and indeed all places of human occupation.

The design of ventilation and air-conditioning systems cannot be touched on within the scope of this chapter, and reference should be made to the literature on this subject. Brief reference can, however, be made to a few of the important items of plant, as follows:

Air Filtration
The removal of the dirt and dust in atmospheric air for ventilation or air-conditioning purposes is a troublesome matter, particularly in industrial cities. Water sprays may be used in the air stream, but it is found that these do not remove many of the oily and sooty particles. Various dry filtering materials are available, such as steel wool, glass fibre, blanket, cotton wool, and paper. These are generally removed and discarded when dirty, and replaced. A newer and more efficient apparatus is the electrostatic filter which depends on the principle of electrostatic charge applied to airborne particles being repelled from surfaces of like polarity, and attracted to surfaces of opposite polarity. Much development work has been done of recent years on improving and simplifying this

71

ELECTRIC PANEL HEATING. 71. *These radiant heating panels in a London shop are suspended by rods from the ceiling and are designed as one feature with the light fittings. The panels are faced with hardboard (Architects: Chamberlin, Powell and Bon).*

72

73

74

HOT WATER HEATING. 72. *High pressure hot water Brightrad (Brightside Foundry and Engineering Co. Ltd.) radiant heating panels in an engineering shop. The plates are of metal and the mean surface temperature is 280°F. 73. Rayrads in the entrance hall of Gatton Secondary School, Reigate (Ideal Boilers and Radiators Ltd.). They give both radiant and convected heat by hot water and are backed by insulating boards (Architects: Adamson, Gray and Adamson). 74. A convector heater for use with hot water (Copperad Ltd.).*

75

76

77

VARIOUS TYPES OF HEATER. 75. *The Vectair (F. H. Biddle Ltd.) is a convection heater for use as a freestanding, semi-recessed or concealed unit operated by high- or low-pressure hot water, steam, gas or electricity and is made in a large number of sizes for all kinds of applications. 76. The Copperad Fan Convector (Copperad Ltd.) combines heating with silent ventilation and operates on steam or on high- and low-temperature hot water. It has a two-speed motor with a change that is either automatic or manual. It is suitable for assembly halls, churches, classrooms, offices and so on. 77. The Luminous Overhead Panel Gas Heater (Bratt Colbran Ltd.) gives visible radiant heat directed where required without loss of floor space and is fixed at from 9 to 12 ft. from the floor. It is suitable for shops, factories, etc. Smaller and larger models are available. 78. Calorier Unit Heaters (Standard and Pochin Bros. Ltd.) in the swimming bath at Woodhouse Grove School, Bradford (Architects: Chippindale and Edmundson). This unit incorporates a fan sending out through adjustable louvres a stream of air warmed by steam or low-pressure accelerated hot water. 79. A close view of a Calorier Unit Heater.*

78

79

80

81

UNIT HEATERS, AIR CONDITIONERS AND PANEL HEATING. 80. *Overhead radiant heating panels using gas (Thomas de la Rue and Co. Ltd. – courtesy South-Eastern Gas Board) fitted high up on the walls of the Camberwell Borough Council's Denmark Hill Library, London. 81. The Aarcon Air-Conditioner and De-humidifier (Longford Engineering Co.) is useful in warm countries where cooling rather than heating of rooms is required. It also cleans the air. 82. The Biddle De-humidifier and Air-cooler (F. H. Biddle Ltd.) is suitable for rooms such as offices in warm and damp climates. 83. A stage in the construction of embedded ceiling panel heating showing the coils laid on the shuttering ready for concreting (seen from above). 84. A further stage showing the coils and slip-tiles which provide a key for the plaster after the shuttering has been struck and before plastering has been commenced (seen from below).*

83

84

82

PANEL HEATING. 85. *Yorcalon copper tubes (Yorkshire Copper Works Ltd.) laid on timber shuttering for a barrel-vaulted roof before the concrete is poured. The tubes, $\frac{1}{2}$ in. in diameter, take hot water and provide well-distributed radiant heat. The plaster laid on them is of special mix and contains a scrim of hessian in the setting coat to prevent surface cracking. 86. Embedded floor-panel heating for a school classroom during construction.*

87

88

BOILERS AND STOKERS. 87. *The American-designed Power-master boiler is now being made in this country (G.W.B. Furnaces Ltd.). It is a fire tube boiler and no site erection is required, the entire equipment being supplied inter-piped and inter-wired ready for immediate connection to electricity, fuel, water and/or steam lines. It is designed to burn either oil or gas and immediate conversion from one fuel to another is possible. It is entirely smoke-free. The picture shows a pair of 250-h.p. Powermaster combination oil/gas-fired boilers. 88. The five gas-fired boilers which serve the heating system of the Royal Festival Hall, London. The system was designed to be as economical as possible under conditions which must respond to rapid changes in demands for heat. 89. Automatic coal stokers firing large La Mont boilers for a district heating system.*

89

OIL PLANT AND DISTRICT
HEATING PIPES. 90. *An oil-
firing plant to a range of heating
boilers. The small boiler on the
right is fitted with a fully automatic burner, while the large
boilers beyond are fitted with
semi-automatic, low-pressure
air burners.* 91. *District heating
mains laid in a trench during
construction. Here the mains are
seen welded together and laid in
position.* 92. *The district heating mains covered with their
lagging and ready to receive
their semi-circular concrete
covers, which can be seen at the
top right.*

90

91   92

93

HEAT PUMP AND REFRI-
GERATOR. 93. *The con-
denser with filter, expansion
valve, economizer and oil
separator of the Royal
Festival Hall, South Bank,
London, heat pump in-
stalled in 1951 and taking
heat from the river water.*
94. *The refrigerating
plant in an air-conditioning
installation.*

94

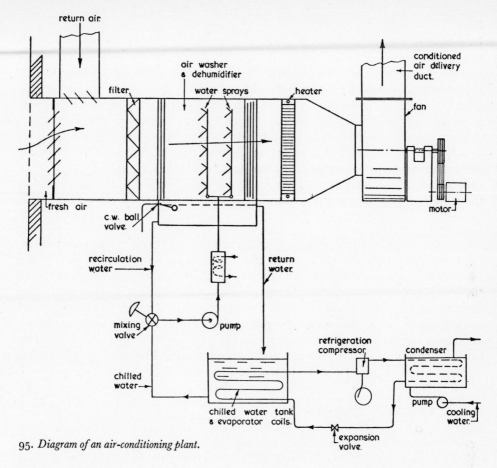

return air

conditioned
air delivery
duct.

air washer
& dehumidifier

filter

water sprays

heater

fan

fresh air

c.w. ball
valve.

motor.

recirculation
water

return
water.

mixing
valve.

pump

chilled
water

refrigeration
compressor

condenser

chilled water tank
& evaporator coils.

pump

cooling
water.

expansion
valve.

95. *Diagram of an air-conditioning plant.*

process, and suitable plants are now available to cover a wide variety of uses.

Air Heaters

Heaters for warming inlet ventilation air may be heated by steam, hot water, or electricity. They are usually of a finned copper type occupying minimum space. Thermostatic control of heaters in any ventilation or air-conditioning system is essential.

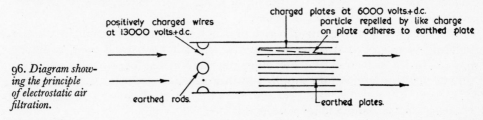

positively charged wires
at 13000 volts.+d.c.

charged plates at 6000 volts.+d.c.
particle repelled by like charge
on plate adheres to earthed plate

96. *Diagram show-
ing the principle
of electrostatic air
filtration.*

earthed rods.

earthed plates.

H

Fans

Fans used in the ventilating of buildings must usually be silent running, though this is not always the case where industrial plants are concerned. The most commonly used type of fan is the centrifugal, in which a runner is arranged in a spiral casing drawing air in along the centre line and discharging it tangentially from the outlet of the casing. Such a fan is usually driven by rubber belts from an electrically-driven motor. Another type of fan, known as the axial flow, delivers the air in a stream in the same direction as the inlet, the fan rotating in a circular casing fixed in the ducting. A third type of fan sometimes used for extraction through roof outlets, etc. when there is little resistance to flow, is the propellor type, which is well known. A fitting often applied to the latter type is the self-closing damper to prevent natural air flow when the fan is switched off.

Ductwork

Large ductwork in buildings may frequently be arranged of builders' work, i.e. by forming suitable ducts and shafts in the structure of the building itself. Smaller ducting is usually formed of galvanized steel or aluminium, but where there are corrosive fumes, as in laboratories, asbestos cement is often used. The design of ductwork is usually a matter of harmonizing architectural design and requirements and at the same time preserving an easy air flow without undue resistance and keeping velocities low enough to avoid noise at the outlets. The arrangement of inlets and extracts and the type of grilles to be employed are all matters which require careful attention on the part of the designer.

13. AUTOMATIC CONTROLS

Brief reference has already been made to the use of automatic controls in connection with boilers and ventilating plants.

The purpose of automatic controls is either: (a) To maintain the desired temperature in individual rooms; (b) To avoid overheating and hence waste of fuel. (c) To curtail heating during non-occupancy periods. (d) To maintain steady conditions of humidity as well as temperature where air-conditioning plant is installed.

The control of a simple central heating system may be sufficiently satisfactory if carried out at the boiler only. It is possible to install control apparatus which adjusts the flow temperature from a boiler according to the external weather particularly where the system of firing is automatic, as with an automatic stoker, oil burner or gas boiler.

The next step is the zoning of a system which would be applicable in a larger building having several different aspects. In such case, each zone could be provided with its own external weather-stat* and means for adjusting temperature of the heating medium supplied in that zone.

* External element sensitive to temperature and wind.

The third method is to provide individual room control in which case every room has its own thermostat and electrically operated valve for controlling the flow of the heating medium to the heating element. Alternatively where forced convectors or unit heaters are employed, the thermostat may be arranged to switch the fan in the unit on or off.

All the above may in addition be controlled by clock switch so arranged as to start the system up sufficiently early to obtain the temperature required when occupancy starts. The design of an automatic control system must allow for the time-lag of the heating system itself and the thermal capacity of the building.

In the case of inlet ventilation systems and air-conditioning systems, as mentioned, controls are inherent and require detailed consideration according to the requirements of each case.

With the growing realization of the importance of efficiency, the use of automatic controls is being taken more seriously than hitherto, and no heating system can be regarded as complete without the inclusion of a proper system designed by a specialist.

14. FUTURE POSSIBILITIES

Looking to the future of heating, it is clear that with the dwindling national resources of fuel, economy in this commodity is likely to become paramount. By appropriate design and selection of building materials, heat losses can, and should, be minimized. Also by the fitting of weatherstripping to windows, and in other ways, it should be possible greatly to reduce air-change losses which are now generally much above what is necessary for ventilation. By the above, and by other means, heating loads will no doubt be much reduced.

Another aspect of this same matter, which is becoming increasingly clear, is that the building and its heating system must be conceived as one machine. The requirements of the building, its thermal storage capacity and hence its time-lag, play an important part in the design, arrangement and selection of the heating equipment, as well as in the type of controls chosen and the timing cycle adopted; also the response rate of the heating system must have a relationship to the time lag of the building.

The future may also hold a change in the use of circulating fluids other than water. It has long been recognized that water, whilst having many advantages, has inherently some disadvantages for the purposes of heating, one being its comparatively low boiling point. Heating fluids have been developed which can be worked at much higher temperatures without correspondingly high pressures, and the only bar to progress at the moment is their high cost. If means could be found of reducing this, a new kind of heating system could be developed using high velocities with small pipes and small heating elements, which might have many applications.

In the matter of fuels, it is possible that atomic energy may, in time, be the normal method, but until this occurs it is difficult to see any change in the present fuel situation. With atomic energy stations there might come large-scale district-heating systems to use the low-grade waste heat, or alternatively cheap electric current might make the use of electrical systems more general. The picture of the future is not yet clear in this regard.

For the burning of fuels in boilers, an increase in boiler efficiency, particularly in the smaller-sized units, can be looked for. One Continental design of boiler, for instance, has a working efficiency of about 90 per cent, and other types of boilers are available for burning solid fuel automatically with automatic de-ashing.

Alternatively, for larger boilers, pulverized fuel is used and this also may become general. It is further open to question whether coal in its raw state will continue as the main source of fuel supply, or whether the future will bring abundant supplies of prepared fuels, so as to make use of the lower grades and smaller sizes efficiently and economically.

Oil will clearly be increasingly used in the future, fuel oil being a product of the petroleum refining processes which are now being carried out on a large scale in this country. So long as petroleum products are imported on the present vast scale for transport, presumably so long also will fuel-oil be available, and for most heating applications it has so much in its favour, with cleanliness and avoidance of labour, that it may take the lion's share of future heating.

Electricity is frequently looked on as the heating agent of the future, but its inherently high cost is likely to prove a barrier so far as can be seen at present.

In general, it would appear that the future trend in the heating of buildings lies in means for reducing heating loads, using boiler plants to serve groups of buildings – if not full district heating, employing a medium other than water or steam – and developments in radiant heating technique. Boiler efficiencies will no doubt rise, and make use of the more refined fuels with automatic firing and controls which reduce labour.

The use of air-conditioning in industry will undoubtedly continue to increase as new processes are evolved demanding an accurately controlled atmosphere. Air-conditioning will also in time presumably become an essential requirement in hospitals, health clinics, laboratories, and in places of amusement where crowds foregather, but it will probably always be regarded as a luxury for conditioning buildings in general for comfort in the climate of this country.

BIBLIOGRAPHY

Basic Principles of Heating and Ventilation. T. Bedford. (H. K. Lewis, 1948.)

Computation of Heat Requirements of Buildings. (Institution of Heating and Ventilating Engineers, 1950.)

Efficient Use of Fuel. (Her Majesty's Stationery Office, 1944.)

Heat Pumps and Thermal Compressors. S. Davies. (Constable, 1950.)

Heating and Air Conditioning Equipment for Buildings. F. B. Turpin. (Pitman, 1948.)

Heating and Air Conditioning of Buildings. O. Faber and J. R. Kell. (Architectural Press, 1951.)

Hot Water Engineering. E. Molloy. (Newnes, 1949.)

Modern Air Conditioning, Heating and Ventilation. W. H. Carrier, R. E. Cherne and W. A. Grant. (Pitman, 1953.)

Modern Principles of Heating and Ventilation. T. Bedford. (H. K. Lewis, 1937.) O.P.

Oil Heating Handbook. H. A. Kunitz. (Constable, 1947.)

Practice and Theory of Radiant Heating. R. M. Starbuck. (Starbuck and Sons, Hartford, Conn., U.S.A. 1949.)

Principles and Practice of Heating and Ventilating. A. C. Pallot. (Newnes, 1950.)

Tables of Hygrometric Data for Air. (Institution of Heating and Ventilating Engineers, 1942.) O.P.

Thermal Properties of Buildings. N. S. Billington. (Cleaver-Hume Press, 1952.)

Ventilation and Air Conditioning. E. L. Joselin. (Edward Arnold, 1947.)

HOUSE HEATING *C. C. Handisyde*

1. GENERAL REQUIREMENTS

By house heating is meant the total services required for heating, hot water supply and cooking.

Recent developments in house heating fall into two rather distinct classes. There have been new ideas in methods of heat distribution and in heating appliances but, governing these, and therefore in some ways more important, are the basic requirements. These basic requirements which are better understood than they were a few years ago are also affected by economic changes so that it is perhaps useful to look broadly at this side of the picture before discussing changes in heating systems or appliances.

Six things seem worth referring to as general factors affecting the methods and appliances to be chosen for domestic heating: (1) comfort conditions; (2) convenience; (3) costs; (4) fuel supplies; (5) insulation; (6) planning.

Comfort Conditions

It is now fairly generally recognized that the mere provision of heat does not necessarily result in real comfort. Heat is lost from the human body chiefly by convection and radiation and, for real comfort, there must be some balance between the losses from these two causes. There have been numerous papers dealing with this question but briefly the findings can be summed up in a few general rules:

(*a*) The total loss of body heat must be limited.

(*b*) A room is not comfortable if the surface temperatures of walls, floor, and ceilings are much lower than the air temperature in the room. Ideally the surface temperatures should be slightly above the air temperature but this is difficult to achieve.

(*c*) There should not be high temperature-gradients from foot- to head-level, nor should wide divergencies in temperature occur across the room.

(*d*) There is a less definitely agreed feeling by some people that a *completely* even temperature throughout a room may give a rather dull, lifeless feeling.

(*e*) There must be an absence of noticeable draughts.

(*f*) There must be some air change or air movement to ensure 'freshness'.

From these rules certain general deductions can be drawn, though it must be remembered that other considerations such as cost may affect just how far one can go towards providing maximum comfort.

Methods of heating will affect relative surface and air temperatures but in all methods good structural insulation of walls, floor and roof will help not only to conserve heat but also to avoid cold surfaces to which excess radiation from the body will occur, resulting in a feeling of coldness unless air temperatures are kept very high as compensation.

Temperature-gradients are very largely influenced by the method of heating. Broadly one can say that methods using convection tend to mean high temperature-gradients vertically. Radiant heating will usually result in low temperature-gradients vertically; but if it emanates from a single, small-area, high-temperature source it may give poor heat distribution horizontally. This often happens with an ordinary coal fire.

If the theory that perfectly even temperatures are monotonous is correct, it probably means that ideally there would be some method of providing a fair degree of heat throughout the room and that this would be supplemented by one or more 'warm spots' which would probably be best if provided by some form of radiant heat of moderately high temperature. Reliance upon small-size, high-temperature radiant sources alone, for example gas or electric fires, appears to result in conditions not ideal for comfort.

Absence of draughts is important. These may be caused by badly-fitting doors and windows and the relationship of these to air-exits such as flues. Excessive ventilation may also occur from these causes and lead to waste. Tests have shown how valuable weatherstripping of external doors can be in eliminating this cause of waste and discomfort. Such weatherstripping and the provision of windows which fit well can reduce heat-loss by 10–15 per cent. Draughts can also be caused by large areas of single glazing and it is for this reason that heating surfaces are sometimes placed under or near windows. In a reasonably well heated smallish room it is questionable whether this point is serious enough to justify any great addition to the expense but it is a point which should be considered when the system permits the easy placing of extra heat near the window. From an economy point of view one must also remember, however, that a source of convection heating under a window may lead to appreciable waste if the window is opened. Double glazing of windows, although it would add appreciably to comfort, usually cannot be justified on grounds of financial cost for houses heated to normal standards in this country – though it will probably come in time.*

The amount of air change required to give a feeling of freshness is much less than that obtained by fortuitous ventilation in most old houses. Careful detailing of fireplaces and their flue openings and attention to weatherstripping of windows and doors should lead to economy without any reduction in comfort.

* See the section on Glass in *New Ways of Building*, Architectural Press.—Ed.

Experiments at Abbots Langley by the Building Research Station showed that in small houses the heat required to make good the losses by ventilation cost over 5s. per week. Too much ventilation is therefore an expensive fault. A well-built small modern house with good windows and weatherstripping to external doors will still have an air-change rate of something like 2 to 3 per hour.

To obtain a comfortable rate of heat-loss from the body there must be a correct degree of heating. It seems that the old standard of heating provided by an open fire, which gave high temperatures over a small area of the room, is no longer considered satisfactory. Various suggestions have been made for standards of heating in living rooms and other rooms and a system of 'background warmth' throughout the house or dwelling has been advocated. The whole question of standards of heating is usually bound up with economy and, for many years yet, is likely to remain so. Nevertheless it is as well to consider what people would *like* even though at present it may not be possible for them always to have it. It is on this question of likes that there seems to be a gradual change taking place. In this country it has been common practice for engineers to design heating systems to give an air temperature of 65°F. with outside temperature at 30°F. and it seems to have been fairly generally accepted that an air temperature of 65°F. is in fact comfortable for rooms where people are sitting for considerable periods. In other countries, and notably in parts of the U.S.A. one normally finds that air temperatures are kept very considerably higher, often at 70–75°F. and sometimes even more. It is also fairly normal for the Britisher to refer somewhat scornfully to people abroad living in overheated conditions. It may well be that in this country we do not require such high temperatures because our climate is different and because we dress differently in winter but it may also be true that a taste of something leads to a liking for a little more and there is some evidence to suggest that as more and more houses are becoming rather better heated and as more and more people get used to working in well-heated offices and factories they are gradually developing a taste for higher temperatures in their homes. It is not unreasonable therefore to suppose that the ideas of to-day will soon be out out of date and that we will all quite soon *like* at least 70°F. in our homes. Although the Abbots Langley experiments showed that temperatures were governed by costs they also showed that in living rooms an air temperature of over 65°F. was common during periods when the living rooms were in use and it was deduced that 'comfortable' conditions in living rooms were judged by the tenants to have air temperatures of nearly 70°F. It is perhaps worth noting also that these tenants were mostly in the under-40-years age-group. It might well be that older occupants would have preferred even warmer conditions.

Convenience
In all types of housing the elimination or reduction of dirt and dirty jobs has become more and more sought after. If costs could be ruled out, almost every-

one would welcome some form of automatic heating, provided it could be really comfortable – with the possible addition of one open fire for occasional use. With total electric or gas heating usually ruled out by cost or other reasons there is still a desire to improve convenience and this means consideration of continuous burning appliances, easy and clean methods of ash removal and, sometimes, planning changes such as placing a boiler out of the kitchen itself. The use of electricity or gas to heat water in summer is now becoming fairly general partly for the same reason and, even in the traditionally coal-burning areas in the north, gas or electricity is becoming quite common for cooking.

Costs

It is absurd to consider house heating without looking at the complete costs involved. Complete costs mean both capital and running costs. Unfortunately, however, in municipal housing since the war the desire to keep down capital cost has been so strong that long-term economies have largely been ignored. This is especially noticeable in the lack of good structural insulation. A more proper evaluation may be possible in private housing and with increased, and still increasing, fuel prices a number of things not previously worth while are now becoming economically advantageous. This should lead to appliances of higher quality, more automatic controls and better insulation – particularly of the structure but also of parts of the heating installation.

From what has already been said it will be obvious that, however desirable certain standards of heating comfort and convenience may be, in much of the housing which is going up now, and will go up in the next few years, there will have to be a balance between income and total heating cost. Some schemes for district heating* in densely populated areas, for example, may show that for a certain standard of heating this method is economical; but if it means that a family is committed to paying a fixed price for the service it may be bad socially because it may lead to enforced shortage of some other vital thing, such as food. Any system which involves a fixed price has the disadvantage that a family suddenly hit by bad times cannot make a temporary economy. Some systems of heating, hot water supply and cooking provide a service which, though far from ideal, *is* very cheap and for certain types of housing the fact may have to be faced that this is all that can at present be afforded. Costs must therefore be considered from the user's point of view and will inevitably influence both standards and types of heating.

Fuel Supplies

Leaving aside oil, which seems unlikely to be used to any appreciable extent, gas, electricity and solid fuel should be considered and they should be considered on a national as well as a personal basis. Although gas and electricity are extremely convenient they are, at present prices, more expensive than solid fuel

* See page 89.

for heating and hot water supply in houses, except during the summer months. Enthusiasts may argue that the very rapid control which is possible with electricity and gas reduces the amount of heat input required because heat can be turned on for very limited periods, but present evidence suggests that, except for cooking and for heating water in summer, gas and electricity can only be used economically as a means of 'topping up'.

Unfortunately since electricity cannot be directly stored, the use of it for topping up may cause an unwanted increase in peak load. Whether this can be overcome or whether eventually some legislation will have to be made in the national interest remains to be seen. For the time being it seems that solid fuel will continue to bear the main load of domestic heating and hot water supply in winter.

The Simon Report* advocated a national fuel policy working towards the elimination of atmospheric pollution by increasing supplies of smokeless fuel. Many appliances capable of burning smokeless fuels such as coke and anthracite are now made but adequate fuel of the correct type is not always available, even at present-day restricted rations, and if present trends continue the shortage of smokeless fuels may become acute. This may have to be taken into consideration in choosing appliances in the future unless a really large change in fuel policy is hastened forward.

Insulation

Since economy is so obviously a key factor in nearly all domestic work it seems obvious that an examination should be made of the economics of reducing heat requirements by providing better insulation. Certain standards have been recommended by the Egerton Committee† and others and there are minimum standards laid down in the Housing Manual.‡ It seems probable that the Housing Manual standards are arrived at by calculating what can be done without any additional building cost rather than by calculating what would be economical. Figures from B.R.S. tests seem to show that running costs are virtually fixed by what the tenants can afford but this does not invalidate the argument that more insulation may be worth while in providing conditions of better comfort for a given expenditure on fuel. Whether this is a good thing when any extra capital cost means an increase in rent is an arguable point. For higher-income housing the decision should be easier to make. The conclusions from the Abbots Langley experiments seem to be that for small houses, with present-day methods of heating, structural insulation should be such as to give U values of 0.20 to 0.25. These values can be obtained quite easily be using a light-weight block for the inner leaf of cavity-wall construction and by insul-

* *Domestic Fuel Policy*. Ministry of Fuel and Power (H.M.S.O., 1946).
† *Heating and Ventilating of Dwellings*. Post-War Building Studies, No. 19 (H.M.S.O., 1945).
‡ *The Housing Manual Technical Appendices*. Ministry of Works and Ministry of Local Government and Planning (H.M.S.O., 1949).

ating the top floor ceiling with a layer of slag wool, glass wool or aluminium foil. There should not be any appreciable increase in the cost of such wall treatment but the roof insulation may add between £5 and £10 per house. In non-traditional forms of construction even better insulation values can often be obtained very economically.

Planning

An important development in recent years has been a wider recognition of the relationship of heating and planning. The outstanding point here is the possibility of using an open plan if full heating is installed. Unfortunately some people at present appear to have been attracted by the open plan for its own sake without appreciating the vital importance of providing adequate heating to go with it. The error which can easily be made is to fail to see the difference between merely combining living room and dining space and the really open plan in which the stair opens off the living room.

It is in the latter type of plan that special care is needed to provide enough heat to deal with the amount which escapes up the stair to heat the first floor. A detailed but important planning point is the growing realization of the heat economy obtained by keeping all flues on interior walls. With some types of plan this may raise difficulties, especially when the water heating is by a back boiler from the living-room fire; the combination of good planning, short hot-water circulation-runs and an interior flue is not always easy to obtain without placing the fireplace too close to doorways for comfort.

With these general points in mind it is possible to consider what heating developments have occurred in recent years and what future changes might take place. These fall into two main categories: (i) new systems of heat-transfer; (ii) new or improved appliances.

2. SYSTEMS OF HEAT TRANSFER

In this country there has been comparatively little development in the methods of heat-transfer used for small houses. The vast majority are still heated by some form of fire or stove in one room with or without the aid of a separate solid-fuel boiler or other hot-water heating-appliance. Perhaps the greatest change, though one which has been taking place for so long now that it is hardly recognized as such, is the adoption of gas or electricity for cooking. Certainly on grounds of convenience, and in most cases also of economy, this is a welcome change and is now common practice in almost all cases except where such services are not available and in some northern districts where the tradition of the solid-fuel cooker is only dying slowly. It seems that a triple-purpose appliance, giving heating, hot water and cooking is unlikely to be really satisfactory by modern standards and it does not give a very high efficiency.

In a comparatively small number of houses full heating by radiators has been installed but in many houses the modern type of open fire or stove with back boiler is efficient enough to serve a small amount of radiator heating surface; and the use of one or two small radiators is increasing. Although this is a convenient and moderately inexpensive way of providing some additional background heat from a single appliance a word of warning is perhaps needed about the possibility of the furring-up of pipes and radiators on such systems in hard-water districts unless an 'indirect' system is used. The idea of heating by radiators is not new but one or two interesting points have emerged. First is one which applies to other systems as well as to radiators. In many post-war houses where an attempt was made to give 'background heat' to the whole house and where the main heating appliance was in the living-room, the background heat was supplied to bedrooms. The B.R.S. house-heating trials in occupied houses suggest that in fact it is much more important to provide such heat in the kitchen. Bedrooms which were 'unheated' did not lead to complaints *in houses reasonably well insulated* provided there was a reasonable temperature in the downstairs rooms. A small, but quite important, point about radiators in small houses is where they are placed. If they are spread about under windows in the manner traditional in larger buildings the cost is usually considerably higher than it is likely to be if they are closely grouped, and experience shows that in small rooms the position of the radiator is not a vital factor.

In rather larger houses the size of piping to a radiator system is larger and the piping can be both costly, unsightly, and sometimes difficult to accommodate easily in the construction. In America it is quite usual even in moderate-sized houses to use a very small accelerating pump. This has the great advantage of making small pipe-sizes feasible. In this country the idea of using a pump on small heating systems has not yet met with any popularity, but for the moderate or large house it is a development well worth investigation.

Of new ideas in methods of heat-transfer so far tried in this country four seem worth mentioning: (1) floor panels; (2) ceiling panels; (3) warm air to the rooms; (4) skirting panels.

Floor Panel Heating
Panel heating is by no means new to this country, indeed the system was invented here, but its use for heating small houses is comparatively recent, and still very limited, although in America it appears to have become extremely popular. Recently in America a good deal of floor panel heating has been done with warm air as the heat source, and sometimes a combination of warm air panels and warm air inlets to the rooms has been used. In this country floor panel heating has been by water, often using a light-gauge small-bore copper pipe as the material for forming the heating coils. Properly designed, and using simple controls, it appears that this can give an extremely comfortable result at a moderate price though not at a price which could be paid at present for public authority housing. A fairly full description of this system with illustra-

tions was published in *The Architects' Journal*, February 19, 1953. Floor panel heating of any kind involves some care in the choice and laying of floor finishes but, with surface temperatures kept to between 75° and 70°F. and preferably near 70° for comfort except at the perimeter of the room, there is a reasonable choice. Thick plywood on battens has proved satisfactory and carefully laid wood blocks seem to be possible. The newer types of composition tile also appear to be suitable, though a certain amount of denting may occur from chair legs or heavy furniture. With these moderate surface-temperatures it may be difficult to obtain adequate heating if a room has very large windows or a very exposed situation. In such cases good structural insulation or possibly some additional method of topping up the heat in very cold weather might become necessary. Floor panel heating plus a small open fire is a most comfortable combination for a living-room. It seems that insulation beneath the ground floor panels is not required but that some edge insulation around the external perimeter of heated floors may be worth while because the heat loss increases when the floor slab gets near to the greater exposure around the edges of the building.

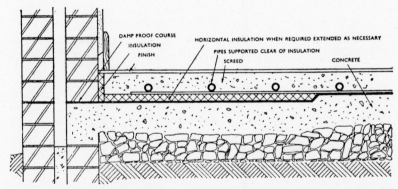

97. *Panel heating; a floor on made-up ground with membrane either sufficiently protected by insulation or of a type not readily damaged nor affected by local heat. This type of arrangement is often used on dry sites without the membrane. (An illustration from 'Panel Heating; Some Practical Applications' by H. H. Bruce in Journal of IHVE.)*

Ceiling Panel Heating
There are a few examples of ceiling panel heating in houses. Some have been carried out with water-heated coils and some by forming a ducting system by which warm air circulates in the first-floor space and heats the ceiling – and to some extent the floor above. Warm-air panel systems where a light ceiling forms the panel surface have the advantage of low thermal capacity and therefore a quicker control than is possible with water panel systems, and a much quicker control than with water panels in a dense concrete floor. It is doubtful,

113

however, whether any ceiling panel heating system will be entirely satisfactory in domestic rooms of the usual present-day height. Opinions differ on this point but there is at least some evidence to suggest that sufficient heating for cold weather conditions cannot be obtained without a feeling of unpleasantness resulting from warm panels so close to head level.

Warm Air Heating

Heating by direct warm air circulation to rooms either by natural or forced circulation is very common in much of North America and since the war a few such systems have been used in Britain. Primary heating may be either by solid fuel or gas but because basements are unusual in our houses the systems employed here have been of the forced circulation type. Two methods have been used. In one the heat is supplied by a normal water-heating boiler. The other method uses an arrangement in which a furnace flue is designed as a heat

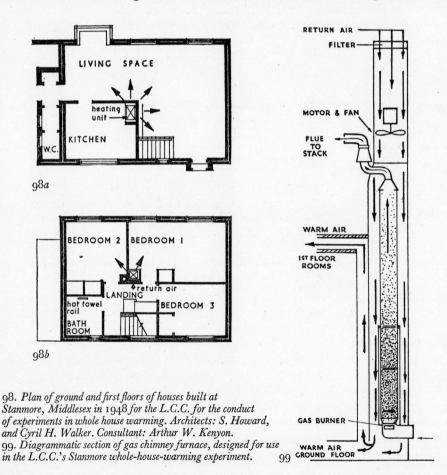

98. *Plan of ground and first floors of houses built at Stanmore, Middlesex in 1948 for the L.C.C. for the conduct of experiments in whole house warming. Architects: S. Howard, and Cyril H. Walker. Consultant: Arthur W. Kenyon.*
99. *Diagrammatic section of gas chimney furnace, designed for use in the L.C.C.'s Stanmore whole-house-warming experiment.*

114

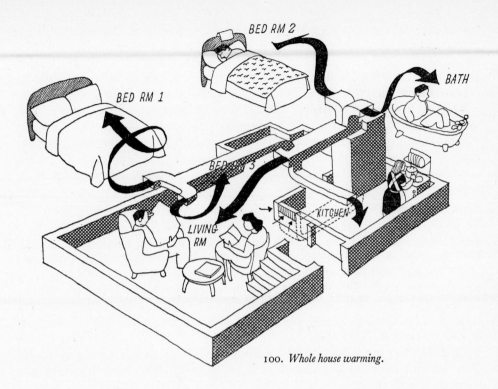

100. *Whole house warming.*

exchanger and warms the air directly. The warmed air is then blown by fan to selected positions, the number and placing of which depend upon the type of house plan and the degree of heating desired. Although this type of warm-air furnace appears straightforward and simple and seems to be economical in running cost it is rather expensive to install. The solid-fuel type has the advantage that it will burn most types of solid fuel and with very little smoke.

Skirting Panels
There are very few examples so far of skirting panel heating in this country. The method has been used to a moderate extent in America and extensive tests at the University of Illinois suggest that it can be both pleasant and economical. The system may be almost wholly radiant or a mixture of radiation with a fair degree of convection. The heating unit consists of a number of sections of cast iron or pressed steel members joined together to form what looks like a rather high skirting. Even in much colder conditions than we get in this country it gives adequate heating and a comfortable result with very even temperature-gradients. The piping runs are not difficult to install but may require a little care in arrangement for both economy and unobtrusiveness and in a mild climate when the full perimeter of a room does not need to be fitted with panels

something may have to be done to the remaining length of 'skirting' to keep it in harmony. The system can be run with small pipes and a pump but has been found to work quite well with natural circulation. With the units not readily available here it is difficult to judge on comparative first costs but it might be expected to be similar to or very slightly above the cost of a comparable amount of radiator heating. It is surprising that a system which combines comfort with such an unobtrusive appearance has not been adopted more for medium-cost houses. Possibly a return to more private house-building will encourage further trials of this system.

3. APPLIANCES

To some extent the types of appliance to be used will have been decided by a general consideration of the heating method to be adopted. For example it may have been decided to have living-room heating by some form of open fire and to use the same appliance for providing winter hot-water supply or it may have been decided to install full house heating by radiators which will require an independent boiler. A considerable number of combinations of heating, hot water and cooking appliances is possible but the commonest choice will be from one or more of the following:

(a) Solid fuel: open fires with or without back boilers; openable stoves with or without back boilers; closed stoves with or without back boilers; independent boilers.

Cookers with or without combination grates.

Any of the above may be suited to varying types of solid fuel.

(b) Gas fuel: gas water-heating boilers; gas fires; gas cookers; gas water-heaters of either the storage or the instantaneous types.

(c) Electric fuel: electric fires, and other electric heaters; electric immersion heaters; storage electric water-heaters, or instantaneous electric water-heaters.

(d) Oil fuel: unlikely to be used except in special circumstances.

Perhaps the greatest advance in appliance designs has been made in the improvement in appliances for burning solid fuel and to a considerable extent this has resulted from improved facilities for testing. The Fuel Research Station has in post-war years carried out a large programme of testing and this has resulted in the preparation by the Coal Utilization Council of a list of recommended domestic solid fuel appliances* which has been issued to local authorities with instructions from the Ministry of Housing and Local Government that in all new housing work licences are to be issued only if the heating appliances are of certain types specially marked in this recommended list. The result of this

* *Recommended Domestic Solid Fuel Appliances.* (Amended from time to time.) Coal Utilization Council, 3, Upper Belgrave Street, London, S.W.1.

has been a great activity by manufacturers in designing and making appliances of sufficiently improved performance to qualify for inclusion on the list. Unfortunately the standard of performance required before an appliance is accepted in this way is not divulged; the real efficiency is not revealed, so that direct comparison of one appliance against another is still not possible.

The Open Fire

Although the higher efficiency of openable stoves, and some improvements in their appearance, has led to a considerable increase in their use, a 'real open fire' is still the delight of most families and it has undoubtedly a great attraction. It will probably continue to be widely used in spite of some drawbacks. Probably it is in the design of open fires that the biggest advances have been made. These fall into four categories:

(*a*) Ability to remain alight when untended for long periods.

(*b*) Adaptability to burning coke as well as coal and therefore to cause less atmospheric pollution.

(*c*) Provision of convection heating by the circulation of warm air to add to heat by direct radiation.

(*d*) Provision of easier and cleaner methods of ash removal.

The ability to remain alight for long periods depends chiefly upon the size of grate and degree of control of the air supply. Machined finishes and accurate control of air-supply openings are now fairly common and several models are now made with a night control to reduce the rate of burning sufficiently to ensure the fire staying in for at least an eight-hour period. This night control usually consists of some form of hinged damper which covers the fire, leaving only a small air vent sufficient to keep the fire slumbering.

Adaptability for burning various types of fuel is not entirely easy. It depends chiefly upon the design of the fire bars and a proper supply of combustion air. Many of the modern fires will burn alternative fuel of a certain size but some models still have a limited range if performance is to be satisfactory. The list of 'recommended appliances' includes notes on suitable types of fuel for each appliance.

Provision for convection heating is a very big advance and can add greatly to the comfort of a room by spreading the heating beyond the immediate circle within reach of direct radiant heat. There are limitations however to what can be done. Attempts to duct away warm air to other rooms can only be successful if the output of the fire is really more than adequate for the room in which it is placed. On the whole the attempts at heating bedrooms with warm air by convection from living-room fires do not seem to have been very successful. Air supply to convection heaters can come from the room in which the appliance is fixed or from some other source. Where the convected air is to be used only for heating the room where the fire is, it can well be re-circulated from that room. Where convection to other rooms is arranged then transfer of smells from food

I

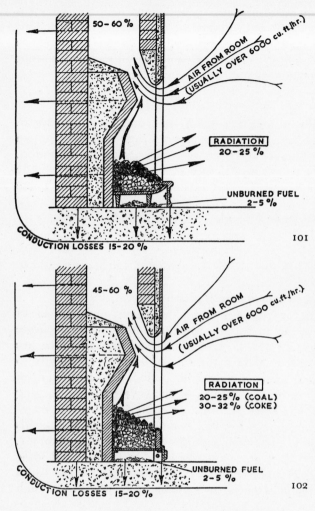

101-106. *Diagrams showing the comparison between the efficiency and performance of types of solid fuel domestic heating appliances.* 101. *Stool-bottom open fire, burning coal.* 102. *Coke grate, burning coke or coal. These two types give lowest test-bench efficiencies and draw off large volumes of air from the room.* 103. *Convector open fire, burning coal or coke: gives higher test-bench efficiency by virtue of convection or 'warm air' heating from the exposed exterior of the appliance.* 104. *Open-close stove, burning coal or coke. When the fire doors are open, the reduced size of the flue outlet controls air-flow; when closed, there is no excessive room ventilation.* 105. *Adaptor fire with restricted throat: a compromise between open fire and stove, suitable for adapting existing fireplaces. Convection heating improves test-bench efficiency, and the throat excludes unnecessary air-flow.* 106. *Closed stove, burning smoke-less fuel: a highly efficient appliance which does not cause excessive air-flow; hence its heat output is fully effective. Most existing stoves of this type are unsuitable for bituminous coal.*

or tobacco smoke might be objectionable and an alternative supply should be provided. It is better for this alternative supply to come from a slightly warm source such as a hall rather than to be brought in direct from the open air.

With all solid fuel appliances proper installation is important but this is especially so with some types of convector fires and makers' full instructions should be obtained and carefully followed.

Some improvements have been made towards easier methods of ash removal, notably the provision of deep ash-pits to hold more than one day's ashes. A tiresome detail which is still often troublesome is the fact that all ashpans are not designed to ensure catchment of all the ash with a result that instead of easy and dustfree removal some sweeping out is also required.

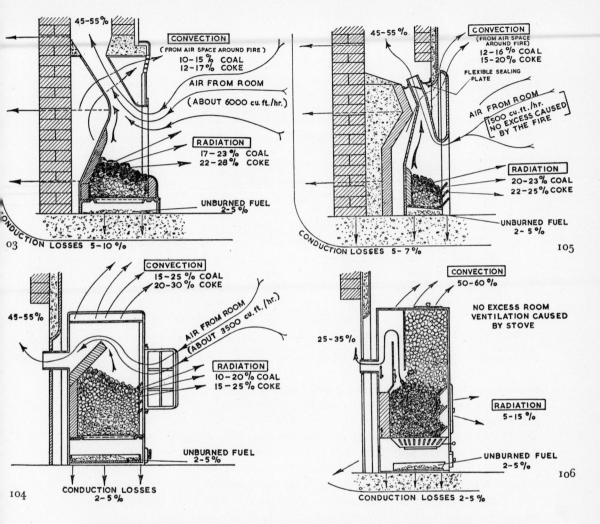

An interesting development is the 'downdraught' type of fire which combines most of the efficiency of a closed stove with much of the appearance of an open fire. In this type the fire is seen as a reflection in a polished metal hood. The latest trend in improving open fires is to endeavour to reduce still further the escape of heat up the flue. It may well be that developments along these lines will become the most important improvement made over the old types of open fire.

Openable Stoves
In spite of the attractiveness of an open fire the higher efficiency of stoves has led to their increasing use, but mostly of an openable type so that some view of

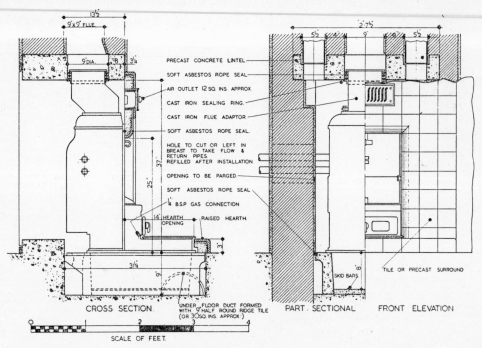

CROSS SECTION

UNDER FLOOR DUCT FORMED
WITH 9" HALF ROUND RIDGE TILE
(OR 30 SQ. INS. APPROX.)

PART SECTIONAL   FRONT ELEVATION

PRECAST CONCRETE LINTEL

SOFT ASBESTOS ROPE SEAL

AIR OUTLET 12 SQ. INS. APPROX

CAST IRON SEALING RING

CAST IRON FLUE ADAPTOR

SOFT ASBESTOS ROPE SEAL.

HOLE TO CUT OR LEFT IN
BREAST TO TAKE FLOW &
RETURN PIPES
REFILLED AFTER INSTALLATION

OPENING TO BE PARGED.

SOFT ASBESTOS ROPE SEAL

1/4 B.S.P GAS CONNECTION

14" HEARTH OPENING   RAISED HEARTH

TILE OR PRECAST SURROUND

SKID BARS

9x9 FLUE

9 DIA

SCALE OF FEET

107. Allied Iron-founders' 'New Marathon' convector open fire – a sunk-ashpit model with boiler.

the burning fuel can be obtained when desired. As with fireplaces they can be used either with or without water-heating boiler attachments. They are available either as built-in or as free-standing models – the latter usually being most convenient for installation into old houses. The free-standing model is also rather more efficient and if an inset type is used it is better to restrict it to the job of heating only the room in which it is placed because the amount of convected heat which can be obtained is less than from the free-standing types. The efficiency of both inset and free-standing models is greatest when used with the doors closed. A point to watch is accessibility for flue cleaning as many of the built-in types are difficult or impossible to clean from the front and some arrangement for back or side access may have to be provided. Although considerable improvements have been made in the design of this type of stove it is probably true to say that much of the objection which some people still have to them is on the grounds of appearance.

Closed Stoves
Although widely used on the Continent and in much low-cost housing in Canada and the U.S.A., the closed stove is comparatively little used in small domestic buildings in this country and there have not been any recent developments of importance which lead to a likelihood of increasing use in the future.

Independent Boilers

Apart from much better design for appearance a number of other improvements have been made to domestic boilers. Better insulation and better controls are fairly general and on many types a wider range of fuels can be burned. The more spectacular developments have been in the introduction of gravity feeding. These gravity-feed types are very efficient but are usually only suitable for one type of fuel and often only for a small graded anthracite which under present conditions may not always be easy to obtain. Some types have an electric blower to supply primary air. Although extremely efficient, and very economical in running cost, these boilers are considerably more expensive in first cost than the more usual hand-fired types.

In small houses where hot water demand is not large it will usually be found economical to shut down independent boilers in summer and to heat water by some form of gas or electric heating.

Solid Fuel Cookers

Although in some districts, especially in the north, the combination of cooking with space heating is popular there are obvious drawbacks to this in most areas in summer. From the trials at Abbots Langley it seems that cooking can best be done by gas or electricity except in country districts where there are no supplies and that in such cases a free-standing solid-fuel cooker is to be preferred. Dual-purpose appliances can give a reasonable service but the triple duty of cooking, space-heating and water-heating is too much to expect from one appliance if an adequate service is required, and it is doubtful whether the apparent economy of providing three services from one appliance is really achieved in practice.

Developments in solid-fuel cookers have been in matters of detail rather than on any major points except that, by giving them a moderate degree of insulation, their efficiency has been improved and their discomfort for summer use reduced. The highly insulated heat-storage type of cooker is popular and very economical to operate but is expensive in first cost.

Gas and Electric Appliances

Gas and electric appliances having been under a more continuous process of improvement, developments in recent years have been rather less spectacular than with solid fuel. Among the points worth noting are the following:

Gas fires have been improved by the introduction of silent burning types and especially by the design of convector models. It is curious that the improved efficiency obtained by the combination of radiation and convection has not been recognized by a wide usage of this type.

Gas water heaters, both instantaneous and storage types, have continued to improve and the introduction of the balanced flue, in which air inlet and flue-gas outlet are adjacent and therefore subject to the same external pressure, makes for much easier and more satisfactory installation and dispenses with the

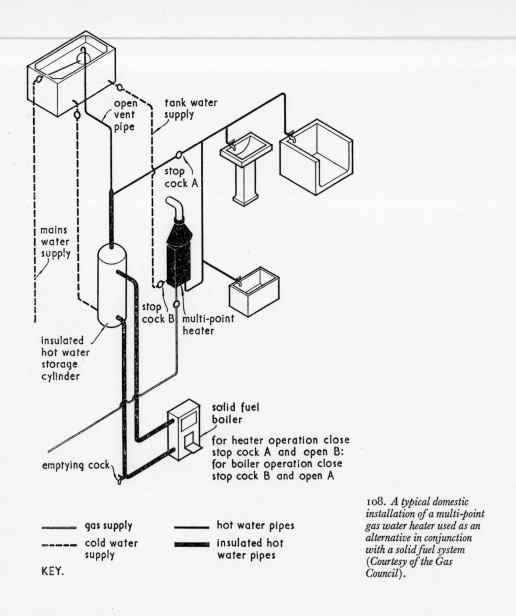

open
vent
pipe

tank water
supply

stop
cock A

mains
water
supply

stop
cock B

multi-point
heater

insulated
hot water
storage
cylinder

solid fuel
boiler

for heater operation close
stop cock A and open B:
for boiler operation close
stop cock B and open A

emptying cock

___ gas supply

----- cold water
supply

KEY.

___ hot water pipes

▰▰▰ insulated hot
water pipes

*108. A typical domestic
installation of a multi-point
gas water heater used as an
alternative in conjunction
with a solid fuel system
(Courtesy of the Gas
Council).*

need for long flues. The small gas circulator as an adjunct to solid-fuel water-heating boilers is also a useful development.

The battle between gas and electricity continues in spite of the nationalization of both. Cookers have improved in minor ways but the apparently logical step of providing a cooker which uses both fuels – each in its most useful way – seems an act of co-operation too difficult to achieve.

A list of tested and approved gas appliances has been prepared by the Gas Council and circulated to local authorities as a companion to the list of solid-fuel appliances; and the British Electrical Development Association has also published a list of domestic appliances.

As stated above, the heating of water in summer is usually more economically and certainly more conveniently supplied by gas or electricity rather than by solid fuel but insufficient attention is given to the need for really good heat-insulation of storage tanks. Storage tanks which are self-contained are usually properly protected in this way but storage tanks heated by electric immersion heaters are often wastefully deficient in insulation. For economical operation they should have three inches of high grade covering, with a loose top cover to permit rapid airing facilities when required. Even with good insulation it is still worth while paying more attention to the size, type and position of immersion heaters than is commonly given. These should always be fitted with thermostatic controls. Although a small 'instantaneous' electric water-heater has been tried there are considerable objections to its use and it is unlikely that the now well-known storage type of electric water-heater will be radically changed. Those which incorporate a small cold-water feed-tank are often quite useful.

Electric fires appear to be mainly of the reflecting type and a new law now makes it compulsory for them to have an adequate front guard device. Space-heating by electric tubular heaters is fairly costly, but cases where their use might well be justified are (a) in a nursery for safety's sake and (b) in a photographer's dark-room, etc. A more interesting possible development is the use of low-temperature panel heating from embedded wiring or other means. This is being fairly strongly advocated in some quarters but the arguments for its use need careful examination in every case before its adoption. It is possible to use electricity in a high-temperature radiant form of heat and thus to take full advantage of the possibility of quick control with its consequent reduction of waste: it therefore seems illogical to use it in the form of low-temperature high thermal-capacity heating when quick control is lost. The argument, of course, is that by this means off-peak loading can be used.

Electrically heated and gas heated 'radiators' with oil filling have also been developed.

Old Houses

Heating methods for new houses can be decided by a careful balance of requirements but the problem of what to do with old houses is often difficult. Where a reasonable sum of money can be spent many of the improved appliances can be used but there does seem to be a real need for some very cheap open-fire fitting with a high standard of performance and capable of being easily and cheaply fitted into existing fire openings. Some other form of convector fire with a restricted flue throat opening is wanted. It is questionable, however, whether an ideal appliance for this particular purpose has yet been produced, though with the considerable attention being given to this problem at the moment it is likely that there will be useful developments in the near future.

4. FLUE CONSTRUCTION

A construction point which is of considerable importance is the type of flue which will be suitable for many of the improved types of solid-fuel appliances. The higher the efficiency of an appliance the lower will flue-temperatures be. This means an increase in the possibility of condensation taking place in the flue, and as a consequence, of damage to the flue lining and possibly to the stack itself. It is therefore well worth while to use an impervious flue lining such as glazed clay pipe but this must be combined with some method of getting rid of any condensate which runs down the impervious lining. Code of Practice 131.101 gives useful detail suggestions on the way such flue linings can be constructed.

5. SUMMARY

One can sum up the trend of domestic heating in recent years by saying that although very considerable advances have been made nothing really spectacular has occurred. The most important points seem to be:

1. A considerable desire for conditions of better comfort and a widespread public interest in ways of obtaining these but, at present, a very definite limitation imposed by the amount people can afford to spend on either first cost or fuel.

2. A very slow appreciation of the value of structural insulation of houses as a means of improving heating conditions or lowering heating costs.

3. A consolidation of the position of solid-fuel appliances as the most generally suitable for the main source of winter heating – coupled with very considerable advances in the design of solid-fuel appliances, especially of those combining convection with radiant heating.

4. A slow but general tendency to relate house heating to house planning.

5. A gradual appreciation of the value of better controls. This shows in the design of fires and stoves and in the use of thermostatic controls on boilers and cookers, and will probably spread to ordinary space-heating much more if conditions improve to an extent where houses can be provided with full heating to proper standards of comfort.

So far as can be seen, for some years ahead small houses will be best provided for if they use one main solid-fuel appliance for space- and water-heating in winter with the appliance big enough to serve a small amount of hot-water radiator surface. Cooking should be by gas or electric cooker and the heating of water in summer also by gas or electricity. Where slightly more expense can be justified or where a rather larger house has to be heated, then a separate independent hot-water boiler may be used and this may serve either radiators,

FLOOR HEATING. 109. *Panel heating coils partly embedded in concrete during construction of the bedroom wing of a small house (Architect: Robert Townsend).* 110. *Leader controls (bottom), circulation pump (right) and mixer (top right) for a floor-heating system in a small house with open planning (Architect: P. de Syllas).* 111. *Boiler and water softener for the same installation.*

109

110   111

112

THREE METHODS. 112. *Floor heating by hot air using inflated rubber tubes to form ducts in concrete floors through which hot air can be passed. (Ductube Ltd.) Here concrete is being placed round the tubing at a house at Caversham, Berks. (Architects: Booth and Ledeboer). The 3-in. tubing is at 6 in. and 12 in. centres and is laid in 4 in. concrete. 113. Skirting heating at a house at Welwyn Garden City (Architect: J. A. Godfrey). 114. A solid fuel cabinet showing external view from kitchen. (115. Interior view.) The cabinet is a self-contained unit designed for economically heating either air and water together, or water alone. The insulated cabinet at the core of the installation contains a furnace operating on the down-draught principle, a heat exchanger, a fan and motor and hot-water storage cylinder with either a gas circulator or other alternative. The heating unit is connected to warm-air ducts.*

114

115

113

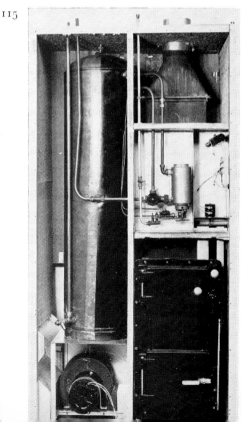

FLOOR HEATING. 116. *The ground floor of the first fully floor-heated house in Britain at 4 Ashley Close, Welwyn Garden City (Architect: W. A. Allen). The general purpose of the scheme was to see whether floor heating could really free planning completely, so far as draughts were concerned, and also to avoid other troubles which could offset the advantages of open planning. A counter containing a small open fire with radiating chimney divides dining space from living space. Heating is by pump-circulated floor panels using $\frac{3}{8}$-in. bore soft copper pipe supplemented by one radiator downstairs. On the first floor the heating pipes are run in the open web joists and are again supplemented by one radiator. A solid-fuel boiler serves heating and domestic hot water.* 117. *Ground floor plan showing pipe lay-out.* 118. *First floor plan.*

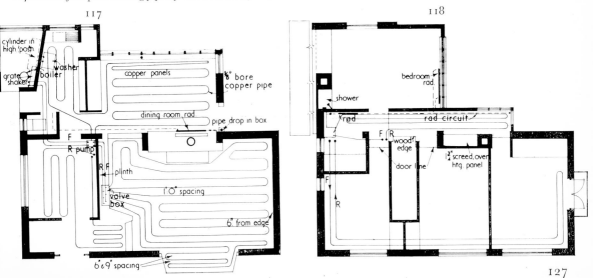

117

118

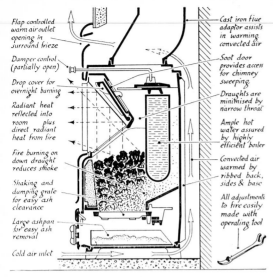

Flap controlled warm air outlet opening in surround frieze

Damper control (partially open)

Drop cover for overnight burning

Radiant heat reflected into room plus direct radiant heat from fire

Fire burning on down draught reduces smoke

Shaking and dumping grate for easy ash clearance

Large ashpan for easy ash removal

Cold air inlet

Cast iron flue adaptor assists in warming convected air

Soot door provides access for chimney sweeping

Draughts are minimised by narrow throat

Ample hot water assured by highly efficient boiler

Convected air warmed by ribbed back, sides & base

All adjustments to fire easily made with operating tool

119   120   121

HEATING UNITS. 119. *Section through a Raymax down-draught convector fire (Radiation Ltd.) which burns solid fuel and contains a boiler.* 120. *Front view of the Raymax.* 121. *The Ascot Multipoint Balanced Flue Gas Water Heater. The system draws the air for combustion from outside the building instead of from within, the whole air and gas system being sealed off from the living accommodation. The heater is built into the wall and a special inlet and outlet flue is fitted behind it with access to the open air. The heater projects no more than 5 in. into the room.* 121a. *Section through the Ascot Balanced Flue Heater showing air circulation.* 121b. *The inlet and outlet flue of the Ascot Balanced Flue Heater seen from the outside of the building.* 122. *A portable electric heater having a metal element deposited within a plate glass panel and therefore being completely safe (Premier Electric Heaters Ltd.).*

122   121a

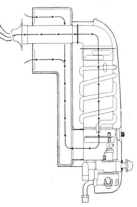

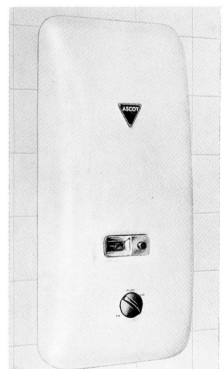

121b

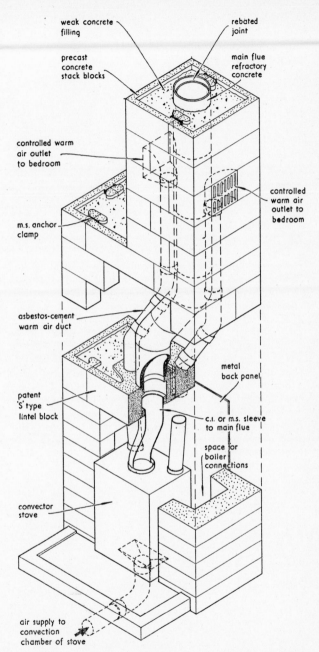

weak concrete filling

rebated joint

precast concrete stack blocks

main flue refractory concrete

controlled warm air outlet to bedroom

controlled warm air outlet to bedroom

m.s. anchor clamp

asbestos-cement warm air duct

metal back panel

patent 'S' type lintel block

c.i. or m.s. sleeve to main flue

space for boiler connections

convector stove

123. *A specialized example of domestic flue construction designed by True Flue Ltd. for use in conjunction with a convector heating stove; a part-sectional view, showing convection heating to bedrooms.*

air supply to convection chamber of stove

a warm-air system or panel or skirting heating. In both cases some provision must be made for 'topping up' by gas or electric fires, both for very cold weather conditions and for the intermediate seasons.

BIBLIOGRAPHY

Domestic Floor Heating. Technical Section. (Architects' Journal, January 31, 1952 and February 19, 1953.)

Economical Domestic Heating. H. G. Goddard. (E. and F. N. Spon, 1953.)

Flues for Domestic Appliances Burning Solid Fuel. (B.S. Code of practice 131.101, 1951. British Standards Institution.)

Heat Requirements of Houses. J. C. Weston. (Journal of the Institution of Heating and Ventilating Engineers, 1951, Vol. 18, No. 185.)

Heating and Ventilation of Dwellings. (Post-War Building Studies, No. 19, H.M.S.O. 1945.)

Heating Research in Occupied Houses. J. C. Weston. (Journal of the Institution of Heating and Ventilating Engineers, 1951, Vol. 19, No. 189.)

House Heating and the Tenant: Experiments at Abbots Langley. Rosslyn Green and Elizabeth A. Milroy. (R.I.B.A. Journal, September, 1952.)

List of Domestic Electrical Appliances. List No. 1. (British Electrical Development Association, May, 1953.)

List of Tested and Approved Gas Appliances. (The Gas Council: revised at intervals.)

Open Fires, Heating Stoves and Cookers Burning Solid Fuel. (B.S. Code of Practice, 403.000, 1952. British Standards Institution.)

Panel Heating: Some Practical Applications. H. H. Bruce. (Journal of the Institution of Heating and Ventilating Engineers, September, 1953.)

Recommended Domestic Solid Fuel Appliances. (Coal Utilization Council; revised at intervals.)

Small Boiler Systems using Solid Fuel. (B.S. Code of Practice 403.101, 1951. British Standards Institution.)

SANITATION, PLUMBING AND HYGIENE

H. G. Goddard

1. INTRODUCTION

The disposal of solid and liquid waste from human habitations is a problem as old as civilization, and probably older. So is the provision of an adequate supply of water. With populations of low density the problems are rarely acute: they become rapidly more so, as density increases: and it is at least as much the concentration of large numbers in a small space as the quest for comfort which has led to the progress made in both subjects in comparatively recent times. Whilst populations were small, scattered, and largely agricultural, the privy and earth closet sufficed for solid disposal, the midden for rubbish disposal and the well or stream for water supply. Indeed, rural economy benefited from such arrangements, for the waste products, returned to the earth, helped to provide the humus and fertilizer which is still, in these days of artificial manures, most valuable; then, it was doubly so.

The destruction of these valuable substances by ill-considered methods of sewage disposal is still a procedure greatly to be deplored: for increasing populations take constantly more from the soil, and it is most necessary that means should be provided to enable them to return as much as possible to it. Some methods of disposal do in fact enable this to be done, and enlightened authorities who have adopted them are able to sell to farmers the valuable product resulting: but there is a strong prejudice on the part of many people against their use: their refined feelings revolt against the consumption of food grown with the aid of human waste products, whilst those of animals can readily be tolerated. The refinement goes further: many squeamishly refuse to buy foodstuffs so grown in this country whilst readily accepting the same foods grown in other countries where such fertilizers are constantly used. The necessity for overcoming such prejudices is of the greatest importance if shortages of food owing to increasing population with decreasing soil fertility are to be avoided: and once these prejudices have been overcome, the authorities responsible for sewage disposal must play their part in ensuring that nothing whatever is unnecessarily wasted.

The two subjects of water supply and waste disposal are very closely connected: the sanitary fittings within the building are the actual point of contact. Upon the number and type of fittings depends largely the quantity of water to be supplied, and the quantity of waste to be removed. The systems providing for both services must be properly balanced if good results are to be achieved. Thus, in many rural districts, water supply from a main source has recently been installed: but the concomitant drainage and sewage disposal schemes have yet to be sanctioned. To install the facilities of bath and W.C. in the houses, with a series of small drainage schemes, each with its own septic tank or cesspit, could only in the long run lead to trouble, and it is better to retain the more primitive arrangements until the complete system can be provided. And, for the time at least, the land will benefit.

The purpose of this chapter is to consider, in the light of present knowledge, how best to supply a building with water; what fittings to use the water in, then how best to remove the water with its load of waste products from the building; and finally, how to dispose of it. Since this is a logical sequence of events, it would equally be logical to follow the same sequence in writing this chapter. Let us, then, start with the water.

2. WATER SUPPLY: GENERAL

Of recent years, a considerable amount of work has been done in this country to improve the quality and quantity of main water supplies, and to make them available to more people, especially in rural areas. In those areas where piped supplies are already available, consumption has tended greatly to grow, and it has become increasingly difficult to make available a sufficient supply. Water has often to be brought to large centres many miles from hilly districts: but the majority of such areas have already been tapped, and strong opposition is frequently encountered, largely from agricultural interests, when fresh fields are sought. The revival of agriculture, and the renewed interest in hill farming in particular, have made more difficult the water engineer's task. To his rescue have come the chemist, bacteriologist and biologist. It is now possible, by suitable treatment, to render safe, and even palatable, supplies which in time past would have been condemned out of hand: in fact something approaching a closed circuit can be used, with water being drawn from a convenient source, treated, used for its many purposes within the building, treated again as sewage, and the valuable products extracted, and returned as effluent to its original source for use again. There are, in fact, cases where this is done: the case is quoted, in *The Purification of Water Supplies**, of the town of Dallas, Texas, which receives its water supply from an artificial lake into which the main inflow is during the rainy seasons of the spring and autumn. During the rest of the time, the only inflow is from the town's sewage plant. In spite of difficulties, scientific knowledge has enabled a safe water supply to be produced throughout the year.

* See Bibliography.—Ed.

Chlorination, first introduced at the end of the last century, remains the main method of sterilizing water: accurate dosage by modern equipment, coupled with modern methods of taste removal, have eliminated the taste so unpleasantly familiar to many during the war. Some risk of corrosion, with heavily chlorinated water, remains. An ozone apparatus has also been successfully used for the purpose. Other treatments received by the water in public supplies are coagulation, to remove suspended matter; filtration, and, where necessary, treatment with algicides; and also, in some cases, hardening or softening. To the architect, these last are the more interesting, for in this country at least, the wholesomeness of a public supply can be taken for granted.

Hardening – generally by the addition of measured doses of slaked lime – is generally undertaken in order to combat the corrosion of metal pipes, and especially of lead service pipes, by very soft water, such as that from peaty moorlands. There is no medical evidence to show that soft waters are in any way detrimental, though certain of them lack trace elements which are valuable, and these may have to be added. Similarly, hard water, once thought to be bad for those with rheumatism and similar complaints, is no longer considered by doctors to have any harmful effect: but softening is undertaken to render the water more pleasant to use for washing, less wasteful of soap, less liable to form scale in boilers and similar apparatus, and better for making tea. A recent official inquiry examined the whole question of the desirability of softening all public supplies whose hardness exceeded a certain figure: the decision was reached that though such softening was desirable, the cost at the present time precludes it. A point which was taken into account is that the chief saving in the home arising from the use of softened water is that of soap: an important point when much laundering is done at home, but one which is at once removed if soapless detergents are used instead, as they now so often are. For these do not react with hard water in the same way that soap does, and make an equal lather whether the water is hard or soft. Their general use may also have some effect on the design of drainage systems: of this, more later.

So much for the water itself: now to consider the pipes which will convey it to the building, and within it.

3. WATER SUPPLY: PIPES

For mains, cast iron or asbestos cement pipes remain in most general use, and they are, of course, used also for the larger service pipes: for the smaller, lead and its alloys, copper and plastic are used.

Recent years have seen the appearance of a number of rivals to the ordinary lead pipe so long used for underground water supply work, for which its ductility and resistance to corrosion made it particularly suitable. Its low strength in proportion to its weight is its undoing, for throughout the world there is a shortage of lead ore; the lead which is produced must be used in the most economical manner, and for those purposes, such as chemical engineering, for which no other material is equally suited.

Two alloys of lead, which by greatly increasing its strength enable much lighter weights to be used, have recently come into prominence: the first is Ternary Alloy, as specified by B.S. 603; this contains 0.25 per cent cadmium, and 1.5 per cent tin: its fatigue strength is three times that of ordinary lead, and for a pipe carrying a given pressure a weight reduction of 30 per cent is permissible. The second is a silver-copper alloy, as specified in B.S. 1085: 1946. Although the quantities of copper and silver are in fact minute – no more than 50 parts per million – the strength of the pipe is so enhanced that weight can be reduced by 30–50 per cent. Yet another way of making use of lead's valuable properties without excessive weight of material is to use a comparatively thin lead tube served with steel strip and overlaid with bitumenized hessian or polyvinyl chloride, a plastic, as a protection against corrosion from the soil.

The other main rivals are copper, which in its dead-soft form is particularly suited to this work; only rarely does the nature of the water make its use undesirable because of corrosion risks, whilst its light weight for a given strength makes handling easy. And, more recently, plastic tubes of the polythene group; these share with copper ease of handling and corrosion resistance and, by virtue of their flexibility, are immune to frost damage, making them most suitable for use in exposed places. Steel tube has of course long been used, with various sorts of protection against corrosion: but comparatively new is the use of electrolytic protection. Most corrosion has been shown to be electro-chemical rather than purely chemical, those parts of the pipe which act as the anode being destroyed. By placing anodes of a less noble metal – for instance, magnesium – adjacent to a steel main, the latter becomes the cathode, and the magnesium anode alone is slowly destroyed, by its sacrifice preventing the destruction of the pipe. The passage of a low-voltage current between anode and pipe makes this action more certain.

An interesting method of pipelaying, now coming into general use for agricultural work, but having many other applications, is the use of a mole plough to form the necessary opening in the ground and to draw the pipe into it, so greatly saving on excavating costs and increasing the speed of laying. A mole plough consists of a wheeled carriage drawn by a tractor, to the underside of which is attached a steel blade carrying at its lower end a torpedo-shaped member, or mole, some four inches in diameter: it is normally used for land drainage work, and the method of using it is to dig a hole, into which the mole is lowered, then to draw it forward: the only mark on the surface of the ground being the narrow slit formed by the blade, which quickly fills. For pipelaying purposes, a shackle and chuck are attached to the back of the mole, to which the pipe is fixed: as it moves forward so the pipe is drawn in after it. Tubes of good tensile strength, flexibility, and long length to minimize jointing are most suitable, soft copper and polythene being outstanding examples. Ordinary steel tube may be laid in this way, though for obvious reasons it is less suitable.

The protection of pipes from frost is worth consideration. Underground, a depth of 2 ft. 6 in. is sufficient to obviate freezing in this country: but, it must be remembered, the pipe must enter the building at this depth. Once within the building, frost protection is largely a question of good planning: but there are occasions when the exposure of a pipe to possible freezing conditions cannot be avoided. The installation of an anti-frost valve is one possible solution of this problem: but best of all is the use of an electric soil-heating cable laid adjacent to the pipe and included in the insulated covering. The electrical supply may be controlled thermostatically, to be switched on as freezing point is approached.

4. WATER SUPPLY: CISTERNS

Similarly, though storage tanks should be protected as far as possible by being placed against chimney breasts, where this cannot be done a small immersion heater, thermostatically controlled, will obviate freezing. An important point, surprisingly often overlooked, is that where ceiling insulation is used, it must by suitable means be carried up over the tank and all pipework possible, so that these are on the warm side of the insulating layer. An insulated lid must be provided. In this way the chances of freezing are minimized: but if the insulation is carried beneath the tank, they are increased. Whilst on the subject of insulation, it is worth while to ensure that, where walls of an insulating material are used for house construction, this material is used for outer walls of the 'outside' W.C., whilst the wall between the main building and the W.C. is of a material – for instance, brickwork – readily penetrated by heat. Once again the risk of frost damage will be greatly reduced.

The extremes of cold met with in parts of North America are undoubtedly amongst the reasons why storage cisterns are little used there: though direct supply from the mains to all fittings is the general practice in the hotter, as in the colder, parts. A question often raised is why in this country we go to the trouble and expense of a storage cistern, when in other countries perfectly satisfactory service is achieved without one. Apart from the risk of freezing, the arguments against the cistern are, that the water therein may become contaminated, either by small fauna falling in, or by absorption of noxious gases from the air; consequently water for drinking should be obtained only from the one tap, specially installed for the purpose, direct from the main. Providing that the tank has a well-fitting lid, and that the water is constantly used and changed, the risk of contamination is in fact very small. There is undoubtedly some saving in pipework, if the connections to all fittings, including the water heater, are taken direct from the main.

The advantages of individual storage cisterns are, however, considerable. In the first place, they balance the load for the supply authority, cutting out sudden peaks in demand, enabling less powerful pumping machinery, smaller mains and service pipes to be used than would be needed if the fittings were served direct. Fluctuations in pressure – a feature of American installations – are cut out. Continuity of supply is assured, even in the event of a failure of the mains. The risk of explosion of water heating apparatus is reduced, since it can be vented direct to atmosphere: and the complication of thermal and pressure relief valves installed on good-class, direct-from-mains systems in the United States, is avoided. Further, the risk of back-siphonage – of which more later – is reduced: and should it occur, it will be limited to the building in which it actually takes place, and not, as can happen where many buildings have all supplies direct from the mains, affect a number. All in all, it would appear wise to follow our well-tried system, rather than to copy those of others. The more so, since, where fittings on a top floor are too high to be served by the cistern, the water authority will generally waive the regulations and allow these fittings to be supplied direct.

5. WATER SUPPLY: COPPER TUBING

Of the water system within the building, perhaps the most interesting feature of modern practice is the widespread use of copper tube of light gauge, with special fittings either of the compression or capillary type. The former have the advantage of rapid and easy erection, with no tools other than a hacksaw and a spanner: the absence of soldered joints eliminates the risk of fire, ever present where plumbers' furnaces and blow lamps are in use. The capillary joint is particularly neat, being scarcely larger than the tube to be jointed. It is perhaps of interest to note that this type of joint originated in the United States, but is not widely used there: its development, and widespread use, has taken place in this country, a reversal of that which takes place in many other fields of engineering.

In some of these fittings, the solder is fed in from the end: but in one make at least, the solder is contained in a recess in the fitting itself, and all that is required is to clean and flux the ends of the tubes, insert them into the fitting, and then apply the blow lamp till the solder appears as a ring round the tube where it enters the fitting. There was a fear amongst skilled fitters and plumbers, when both types of fitting were introduced, that their skill would no longer be needed, and that any handy man could be employed to erect a water system in copper. Their fears were unfounded: rather, the use of these fittings has given a good man a chance to produce an outstandingly neat system in a reasonable time.

A further method of jointing copper tube, excellent where the fitter has the skill to manipulate the tube, and make the welds, is the use of bronze welding with a gas torch. There is little or no saving in cost over fittings, in the smaller sizes commonly found, for instance, in a building of the domestic type: but fittings rise rapidly in cost as the size increases, and for the larger sizes, welding

LAYING WATER PIPES BY PLOUGH. *Laying copper water pipes underground by means of the Yorcalon Mole Plough (Yorkshire Copper Works Ltd.) drawn by a farm tractor. The average speed of laying is* 100 *to* 150 *ft. a minute. The essential part of the mole plough consists of a knife running below ground to a depth of up to* 2 *ft.* 6 *in. – that is well below frost level. The knife displaces the soil to a width of* ¾ *in. To the bottom of the knife is attached the mole, a cylinder which creates a tunnel* 3 *in. in diameter. To the end of the mole is fixed a short flexible wire link to which the copper tube is attached.* 124. *The mole being raised out of a hole at the completion of a* 1,200 *ft. pipe run. A hole into which the mole is lowered is also dug at the start of the run.* 124a. *Transverse- and cross-sectional diagrams.* 124b. *Sectional model. The two main advantages of the system are speed of laying and saving in cost of that trenching required by traditional methods.*

124

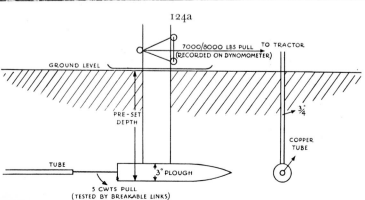

124a

7000/8000 LBS PULL TO TRACTOR
(RECORDED ON DYNOMOMETER)

GROUND LEVEL

PRE-SET DEPTH

¾"

COPPER TUBE

TUBE

3" PLOUGH

5 CWTS PULL
(TESTED BY BREAKABLE LINKS)

124b

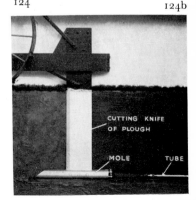

CUTTING KNIFE OF PLOUGH

MOLE   TUBE

125

PIPES. 125. *The Spruce-Thrower Soil Unit (B. Finch and Co.) is a patented cast-iron soil junction component for multi-storied buildings where individual closets are planned one above the other. It eliminates the awkward connection of the anti-siphon pipe, and, as it can be built in as work proceeds, it also eliminates holes which must be made good (see also fig. 147, page 152).*
126. *An impervious pitch-fibre conduit (Key Engineering Co.) for protecting electric cables and also for drainage and effluent disposal. 126a and 126b. A compression sleeve joint of the pipe.*

126

126a   126b

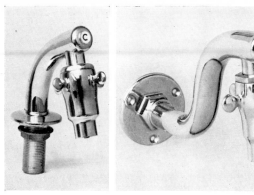

127   127a   127b

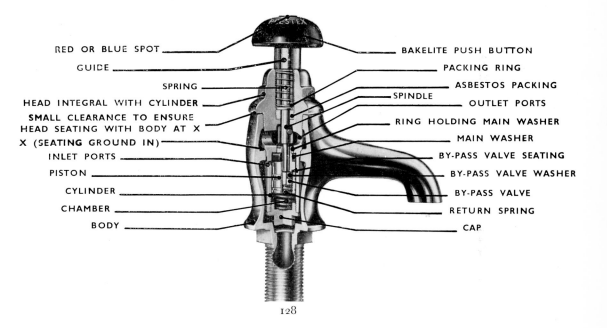

RED OR BLUE SPOT

GUIDE

SPRING

HEAD INTEGRAL WITH CYLINDER

SMALL CLEARANCE TO ENSURE
HEAD SEATING WITH BODY AT X
X (SEATING GROUND IN)

INLET PORTS

PISTON

CYLINDER

CHAMBER

BODY

BAKELITE PUSH BUTTON

PACKING RING

ASBESTOS PACKING

SPINDLE

OUTLET PORTS

RING HOLDING MAIN WASHER

MAIN WASHER

BY-PASS VALVE SEATING

BY-PASS VALVE WASHER

BY-PASS VALVE

RETURN SPRING

CAP

128

129

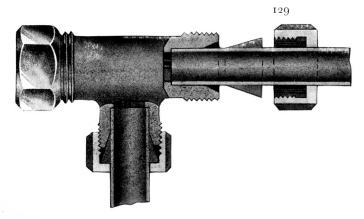

TAPS AND PIPE JOINT. 127 *and* 127a. *Two
designs of Supatap (F. H. Bourner and Co.)
in chromium-plated brass. The washers can
be changed without turning off the water flow
and they also eliminate splash (see fig.* 146,
p. 150). 127b. *Supamix (F. H. Bourner and
Co.) is on the same principle and mixes hot
and cold water as required.* 128. *The Prestex
self-closing, non-concussive spring cock
(Peglers Ltd.) has the advantage that it
reduces water waste and therefore, in the case
of hot water, fuel waste.* 129. *The Kontite
waste pipe fitting for copper tubes (Kay and
Co.) showing a Tee joint, the junction on the
right before being screwed up and that below
after being screwed up.*

130

131

132

133

FITTINGS. 130. *Fireclay circular treadle-action ablution fountains (John Bolding and Sons) for factories and similar buildings where many want to wash their hands at the same time.* 131. *The same type of fountain in use. Water is released when the ring is pressed with the foot.* 132. *A fireclay slab urinal without partitions (Adamsez).* 133. *A fireclay stall urinal with partitions and glass splash guards (Southbrook Potteries Ltd.).*

FITTINGS. 134. *Urinal bowls at Wokingham Secondary School (Adamsez Ltd.) designed to reduce the smell of urine. Projecting lips catch the drips and the waste trap has been inverted to ensure that a fair amount of water remains in the waste pipe to keep the urine in a weak solution. The rear wall and floor are washable and impervious.* 135. *A fireclay urinal slab in the Royal Festival Hall, London, lavatory has anti-splash lips and integral partitions to simplify fixing (Adamsez).* 136. *The lavatories at a Worksop factory (Architects: Cecil Howitt and Partners – courtesy Carter Tile Co.) have a neat, tiled fitting to contain un-sightly plumbing and to support the basins and mirrors.*

135

134

136

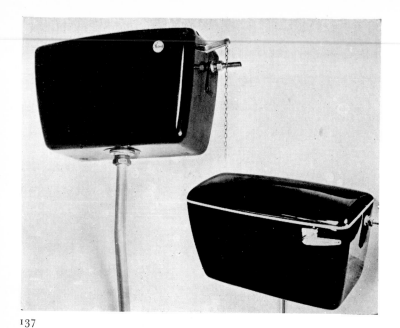

137

138

138. *Cross sections of pans. Top, wash-down; centre, siphonic; bottom, double trap, full bore siphonic (Shanks and Co.).*

139

WATER CLOSETS. 137. *Lynx flushing and low-level cisterns in Duranite, a non-corrosive, pitch-based composition (Shire and Co.).* 139. *A plastic, open-fronted seat (Robert McArd and Co.) of a type which should always be installed in unattended lavatories.* 140. *A new development in pans (Adamsez) has a rimless bowl. Fouling cannot form as under the usual rims.* 141. *A bowl with Bakelite seat, cover and armrests designed by James Gardner (Adamsez).* 142 *(facing page). One of a range of closets, with plumbing neatly concealed behind a tiled partition having access panels, at Becton Welfare Centre (Architect: A. H. Shearing of Brian Colquhoun and Partners).*

141

140

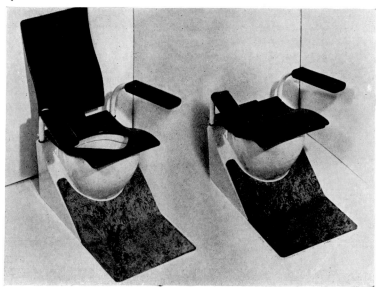

142

143

144

CLOSETS AND A WASTE DISPOSAL UNIT. 143. *Plymax, the metal-faced plywood (Venesta Ltd.) can be used for W.C. partitioning.* 144. *The Destrol chemical closet (Proved and Producing Properties Ltd.) for use where water supply and normal drainage are not available. A mixture of water and sterilizing fluid is pumped up into a flushing cistern from a settling tank and is discharged back into the tank again. Occasionally the tank is drained off into a soakaway and replenished.* 145. *The American Disposall (General Electric Co.) is fixed below a kitchen sink to shred food waste, including bones, into fine particles which can be washed down the waste pipe.*

145

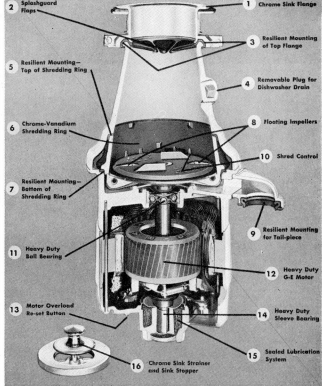

2 Splashguard Flaps

1 Chrome Sink Flange

5 Resilient Mounting— Top of Shredding Ring

3 Resilient Mounting of Top Flange

4 Removable Plug for Dishwasher Drain

6 Chrome-Vanadium Shredding Ring

8 Floating Impellers

10 Shred Control

7 Resilient Mounting— Bottom of Shredding Ring

9 Resilient Mounting for Tail-piece

11 Heavy Duty Ball Bearing

12 Heavy Duty G-E Motor

13 Motor Overload Re-set Button

14 Heavy Duty Sleeve Bearing

15 Sealed Lubrication System

16 Chrome Sink Strainer and Sink Stopper

should show a definite saving. Well carried out, a beautifully neat job is made. In many cases, it will be found best, for ease and safety in erection, to combine bronze welding or capillary fittings with compression fittings.

6. WATER SUPPLY: OTHER PIPES, CORROSION

The use of lead pipe for water services within the building is now limited, except in special cases, to the rising main – though this may equally be in copper – and to the 'tails' connecting a galvanized system with taps: a purpose for which its ready manipulation makes it particularly suitable. The high cost of the lead-tin alloy solder has resulted in the adoption of the spigot joint, in place of the customary wiped joint: it uses far less material, and an equally good joint is made.

Galvanized steel tube remains the most used material for the distribution of water to the fittings in a building, for its cost is the lowest. Its properties, advantages, and deficiencies are so well known that it is not necessary to repeat them here. It may be well, however, to call attention to the risks which are run in mixing copper and galvanized steel in the same system: electro-chemical action is set up, and premature failure occurs. The Building Research Station carried out an investigation, and published their findings in their *Digest No. 8*. The case is quoted of a housing estate of 1,000 houses, where a galvanized cylinder was connected to a copper hot water service. After four years, 50 per cent of the cylinders had failed, due to the picking up of minute particles of copper which had dissolved in the pipes: local electrolytic action was set up, and this destroyed the zinc: once this protective coating was off, the steel sheet rusted through very quickly. For similar installations in which galvanized tube took the place of copper, no failures were reported in six years. It was found that a very minute quantity of copper sufficed to start the action: as little, indeed, as one part in ten million.

The presence of temporary hardness, leading to the formation of scale on the interior surfaces of the cylinder, has a protective effect: and it is recommended that where mixed systems are installed, water softening should not be carried too far. Failures of galvanized steel cold water cisterns are rare, but there is some evidence that to use copper for cold water rising mains and down feeds to hot water systems, of which the cylinder or pipe work are in galvanized steel, is unwise. The safe course is to install all-copper or all-galvanized systems: the latter with a steel or cast iron boiler.

It is most likely that we shall not have long to wait before plastic tube, with either screwed or compression fittings, comes into regular use for internal plumbing: indeed, there is no reason why polythene tube should not be employed for cold water work, save that its flexibility makes necessary a supporting batten for horizontal runs, or at least a pipe clip at about 2 ft. centres. It is not suitable for hot water work, for it softens with heat, and loses tensile strength: a maximum figure of 149°F. as a working temperature is given. Even at this temperature, it would doubtless share with lead the bad habit of creeping. One must, however, look forward to the coming of a reliable, rigid, plastic tube for hot and cold water services, for then many corrosion worries will be at an end.

The possibility of using aluminium for pipework has been explored: in fact, it has been so used in Germany. But without considerably more knowledge of its performance, one would do well to avoid it: many of the impurities found in water are such that they could be expected to cause severe corrosion unless some special treatment were adopted. This might well make the price prohibitive, and would certainly make necessary a very high standard of workmanship, if untreated metal were not to be exposed at the joints. Accelerated corrosion might take place at these points, if they were left so exposed.

7. WATER SUPPLY: CATHODIC PIPE PROTECTION

Mention has already been made of the use of cathodic protection for the outside of pipelines buried in corrosive soil. It is equally applicable to the inside of a system. It has already been explained that most corrosion is electro-chemical, a minute current flowing from one metallic part to another, and dissolving that part from whence it flows – the anode – whilst not affecting that part which is the recipient – the cathode. Where two dissimilar metals are included in a system, the current flows from the more base to the more noble: the former being destroyed in the process, the latter preserved. The greater the electrical dissimilarity, the heavier the current and the more rapidly will the destruction take place. The table below gives a list of some well-known metals, showing their relative position in the electro-chemical series, and their normal electrode voltage:

NOBLE	Gold	$+$ 1.42	Nickel	$-$ 0.25	
	Platinum	$+$ 1.2	Cadmium	$-$ 0.40	
	Silver	$+$ 0.80	Iron	$-$ 0.44	
	Mercury	$+$ 0.80	Chromium	$-$ 0.71	
	Copper	$+$ 0.345	Zinc	$-$ 0.76	
	(Hydrogen)	0.000	Aluminium	$-$ 1.67	
	Lead	$-$ 0.125	Magnesium	$-$ 2.34	BASE

Electro-chemical corrosion may however take place when only one metal is present: for differences in stress or temperature may cause destructive differences in potential.

What must, then, be done to stop this corrosion is to ensure that the current will always flow *to* the metal work of our system, and never *from* any part of it. In the United States magnesium anodes are obtainable for hanging in hot water tanks: this being the most base metal on the list, it will always be negative to the other parts of the system, and thus, as in the case of the external protection, will

146

tend to preserve them. Again, more positive protection is achieved by passing a low-voltage current through the anode: the amount being controllable by a rheostat. Such a system, invented by a Dane and developed in Holland, is now available in this country. Aluminium anodes are used, and the release of the aluminium in the water precipitates the scale-forming salts: thus a dual function is performed. As a further extension of the use of electrolysis, a copper anode can be added which by releasing minute quantities of copper salts prevents the growth of algae and the like. The system is one of considerable potentialities.

The risk of corrosion, serious as it is to the system, and to the pocket, is a risk to health only with lead. But defects in the design of fittings and in the layout of the supply piping can in certain circumstances constitute a serious danger to health by allowing 'back siphonage' to take place, from fittings in which contamination may occur to outlets from which drinking water is likely to be drawn. True, this danger is far more present in the ordinary American type of system than the ordinary system here: but nevertheless, even here the risk must be recognized and remedial measures applied.

8. WATER SUPPLY: FITTINGS AND BACK-SIPHONAGE

The risk of back-siphonage is always present when fittings are used in which the inlets can be submerged, or nearly submerged, before the fittings overflow. If such a fitting is on the upper floor of a building, and the supply of water to that building temporarily ceases – owing, for instance, to the closing of the main stopcock for repairs to be made, or to an abnormally heavy demand – where all buildings are supplied direct from the mains, the drawing-off of water at a fitting on a lower floor will empty the pipework above it, and so produce a negative pressure quite sufficient to draw the water out of the submerged inlet fitting on the upper floor. This water, very possibly contaminated, will then be discharged through the tap at low level: where a number of adjacent buildings are served by the same main, the trouble may not be confined to the building in which the unsatisfactory fitment is situated: the contaminated water may appear at a neighbour's tap.

The degree of negative pressure produced by the siphonage of the water in ordinary pipework in the way described is remarkably high, and tests carried out in the United States have shown that water may be drawn not only out of a submerged inlet, but through an inlet as high as one and a half times its diameter above the level of the water in the fitting.

Clearly, some fittings will be more prone to be trouble-makers in this way than others. Any fitting in which the inlet is $1\frac{1}{2}$ in. above the highest point to which the water can rise can be considered safe, provided that attachments – such as hand-showers or shampoo-sprays – are not connected to the inlet, thus converting it into a potential underwater one. Thus, baths and basins of normal construction present no difficulties. Baths with underwater inlets are to be avoided: so are those with globe taps.

More difficult to deal with are those fittings which from their nature have their inlets below potential water level: such are W.C.s, bidets, and some types of urinal: hospital fittings of various kinds and industrial equipment. But of all risks, probably the worst is in the W.C. with flush valve: the more so, where an additional connection from the valve is used and connected to the trap below water-level to induce siphonic action. Fortunately, such fittings are rare in this country, though most commonly used in the United States. In Britain, devices to prevent back-siphonage, by destroying the vacuum which causes it, are available: but in some cases these vacuum breakers are not completely reliable in action, and may be reduced to inoperation by corrosion. Further, as in some cases they are noisy, or leaky, or both, they are all too often sealed up. The flush cistern is subject to back-siphonage only if the ball valve is fitted with a 'silence tube' without an adequate air hole to prevent back-siphonage. The usual $\frac{1}{8}$ in. hole intended to prevent a depression forming is entirely inadequate: one authority states that not less than half the diameter of the silence pipe is needed: another, that the full diameter is necessary. A T piece, between the ball valve and outlet, will eliminate this, whilst still serving effectively as a silencer.

A frequent question is why flush valves are not more used in this country: they are said to be neater than flush cisterns, to be quieter in action, to suffer less from derangement, and to be ready for use again immediately the first discharge has taken place. Further, they may enable some space to be saved in the room. Of these arguments, the only one which can be accepted is that concerning immediate re-use. A modern 'low-down' W.C. suite is of good appearance, and very reliable in action: and provided only that the precaution just mentioned is taken in respect of the silence pipe, it has the advantage of dissociating the W.C. equipment completely from the remainder of the pipework, and eliminating any risk of back-siphonage. Few water supply authorities in this country will accept the flush valve because, in the event of its going wrong, water will be lost, and no means of giving warning of its failure is possible.

9. FITTINGS: WATER CLOSET

In considering W.C. fittings, special mention may be made of one or two types having particular advantages. In the first place, some modern designs of si-phonic closet – unfortunately high in cost – achieve not only an extremely reliable action but also such a standard of silence that they, and the subsequent refilling of their cistern, are inaudible beyond the compartment. No longer need the 'noise of stubborn machinery' announce its presence. This may be thought of particular advantage when the small space available in modern flats makes the close juxtaposition of the various apartments inevitable. Again, note may be made of the excellent small W.C.s made especially for Junior Schools: and to the improved versions of the trough-flushing cistern, serving a number of fittings, which are suited both to schools and to industrial buildings, and eliminate difficulties resulting from delays in refilling an individual cistern. Their use makes of less importance the one real advantage of the flush valve.

Finally, attention may be drawn to a very neat type of 'low-down' closet in which the flushing cistern, of glazed fireclay to match the bowl, is attached to it and forms, as it were, a back to the seat; the flush pipe is internal and cannot be seen. Fittings of this kind have been met with both in America and in Switzerland and are now available in this country. Whilst it will be readily agreed that points of design of this kind have only the nature of a fashion, and no superiority in action can be claimed over the best of the more conventional type, the neatness of this design cannot be denied.

The tendency towards simple and straightforward design is to be found in other fittings also: it is satisfactory to record that most of the curiously angular designs which manufacturers thought to be modern have given way to more smoothly fashioned, rounded and readily cleaned shapes. Some are claimed by their makers to be streamlined, though one can hardly believe that they were really intended for rapid progress through air or water, for that is what the name implies.

10. FITTINGS: TAPS AND WASTES

Of the ancillary fittings, taps have probably come in for more ingenious but often misapplied development than any other device. Some new designs permit the renewal of the washer without either turning off the water or using an inverted bucket to catch the spray as the top of the tap is unscrewed. This is a laudable point. In one of these designs, the nozzle portion of the tap – incidentally containing an efficient anti-splash device – forms also the control portion: the design is neat but the tendency is to try to close the tap, when turning it on, and vice versa, since the action of the screw thread is reversed. Another type of tap which has very real value in the institutional type of building is the non-concussive, press-down type, wherein a dashpot arrangement ensures slow closing, and consequent absence of water hammer, when the tap is released. Since water flows only when the tap is pressed, waste of water and of heat, due to taps being left running for an unnecessarily long time, is avoided. Again, for institutional purposes, the thermostatic mixing valve, connected to the single tap of a number of wash basins, has considerable advantages.

The use of pop-up wastes, with their unnecessarily complicated linkage, and cleansing difficulties, has fortunately almost died out in this country, although they are still popular in the United States: indeed, it is said that they are demanded there, for folk do not like to put their hands into used water to lift the ordinary plug. Here, our lesser refinement permits the use of the simple and certain plug and chain.

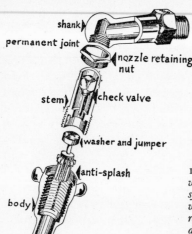

shank

permanent joint

nozzle retaining nut

stem

check valve

washer and jumper

anti-splash

body

146. *A new tap design which permits the renewal of the washer without shutting off either water supply or draining system. The built-in check valve automatically cuts off the water when the nozzle is unscrewed and the washer can then be renewed in a few seconds. The tap has a built-in anti-splash device. ('Supatap' by F. H. Bourner and Co. (Engineers) Ltd.) (See also figs. 127, 127a, 127b, page 139.)*

11. FITTINGS: SHOWERS, BATHS, BASINS, SINKS

Considerable development has taken place in the design of shower fittings. The old-fashioned, wasteful rose has been replaced by the 'economic' type of head which produces a fine spray: further, the old-fashioned erratic mixing valve has gone and in its place we find one with thermostatic control. In the case of a range of showers in, for instance, a school, the mixing valve may be common to the whole range, and under the control of someone in authority. Unfortunately, the shower has in no way achieved the popularity here which it has done in the United States. To change people's habits is difficult; but many are only now beginning to know the pleasures of a fixed 'tub' bath. The saving in fuel to be effected by the use of a shower in place of a tub is great: one usage of the former uses perhaps 5 gallons of mixed hot water, of the latter, 30. If showers could be made generally popular in place of the tub, a vast fuel-saving would result.

New materials for sanitary fittings there are, but none have yet achieved prominence. The pressed steel bath and wash-basin have come and, temporarily at least, gone, because of the shortage of deep-drawing sheet steel. The advantage of such fittings is the lighter weight and resistance to fracture, important with modern handling methods. Plastic fittings have been tried, and it is understood that such baths have been successfully made in the United States: here, a trial prototype failed through softening by heat. There is no doubt, however, that the difficulties will be overcome, and that the fittings of the future will be of plastic material. Aluminium alloy has been tried for sinks, in place of the costly and scarce stainless steel; but soda, still much used for washing-up, blackens it. Pressed steel, with vitreous enamel finish, has provided another substitute; but, by the very nature of its use, a sink runs greater risk of chipping than a bath or basin. Glazed fireclay remains by far the most used material; and, when fitted with draining boards of suitable wood – for preference, teak, with iroko as a second choice – it can still beat most of its rivals.

A very useful fitting for industrial work is the wash fountain, replacing, as it does, a whole range of lavatory basins, and giving the advantage that washing takes place under a spray of running water, and not in a possibly contaminated vessel. Water to these can be supplied through a thermostatic mixing valve, as with showers: and an economy in hot water may be shown when a number of persons make use of the appliance at once. Their use for schools has been advocated by some: but here, the chances of their frequent use by one pupil only is considerable, and basins are likely to prove more economical. The advantage of cleanliness, however, remains.

12. DRAINS: THE ONE-PIPE SYSTEM

Of the subjects discussed in this chapter, drainage has probably made more progress in recent years than the others. The tendency has been towards simplification: some of the precautions, for many years thought essential, and well loved by local surveyors and sanitary inspectors, are now shown by research to be unnecessary and even undesirable. Most of these precautions were based on the fear that foul air from the drains would escape into the house, bearing pestilence with it: and whilst no one will deny that the avoidance of such an escape is most desirable, its evil effect was grossly exaggerated. This fear led to an excess of traps, themselves devices likely to become foul and in other ways to give trouble: the fewer of them, the better.

The most prominent result of this more enlightened policy is the general acceptance of the one-pipe system of drainage, where both 'waste' and 'soil' fittings are connected to a single stack, in place of the two-stack method, with trapped gulley to the waste stack. Except in the case of a small two-storey dwelling, the term 'one-pipe' is a misnomer, for in fact two pipes are needed, the second being a vent stack to which the traps of all fittings are connected, to eliminate the risk of unsealing by siphonage. It is important that the traps should not become so unsealed, for they are the only bar between the air in the drain and that in the house; to reduce the risk, deep-seal traps, with a seal depth of 3 in. are used in place of the more normal $1\frac{1}{2}$ in.

Tests continue, to determine whether in fact the vent stack is as necessary as we now think it to be, for there is no doubt that it is an unmitigated nuisance, with its Christmas-tree-like collection of small branches. Further, the cost of a one-pipe installation may, as a result, be higher than that of a two-pipe system, unless the planning of the fittings is carefully done, to ensure their concentration and their proper placing in relation to the stacks. The saving on the underground drainage – only one branch drain is needed with the one-pipe system against two with the two-pipe – is not likely to cover the extra cost of the overground work, if the plan is at all diffuse.

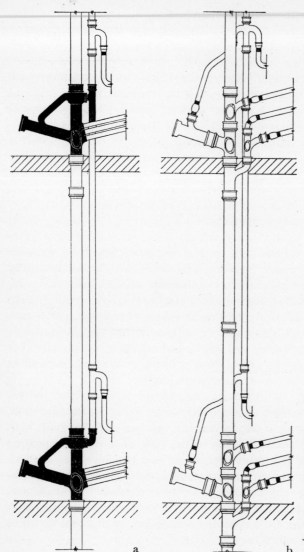

147. *The 'Spruce-Thrower' soil unit is a cast-iron patented fitting designed as a soil junction component which incorporates the anti-siphon branch and eliminates the awkward connection of the anti-siphon pipe between the soil pipe branch and the main anti-siphon pipe.* 147a. *shows suggested layout incorporating the unit cast with sockets to receive sink, lavatory and bath wastes. (See also fig. 125).* 147b. *shows the layout of an actual job using orthodox fittings.*

a   b

Recently introduced special fittings simplify erection and result in a neater and less expensive job. The Spruce-Thrower unit, for simplifying the connections to both stacks, is an ingenious example of such a fitting: further, it can be obtained not only with connections for the W.C., but with screwed sockets for the other branch wastes. A considerable number of joints is thereby eliminated, with a corresponding saving in cost. However, the advantage of such units does not rest with the one-pipe system alone, for special ones are also made for two-pipe systems. Their use for either system can be strongly recommended.

It is in the two-storey dwelling that the one-pipe system – now genuinely one-pipe – can show a saving; for here it has been shown conclusively that the vent stack is unnecessary: provided deep-seal traps are used, the workmanship is good and certain design precautions are taken, there need be no fear that there will be any escape of gases into the house. A further advantage of the one-pipe system over the two-pipe – and this of course applies equally to multi-storey buildings – is that the soil pipe is thoroughly cleansed by the passage of the waste water, and the risk of blockage reduced.

A considerable amount of research has taken place into the behaviour of these single-stack systems, both at the Building Research Station in this country, and abroad, notably in the United States. The subject particularly studied was the possibility of traps on fittings being unsealed, either by induced siphonage – owing to the discharge of other fittings – or self-siphonage – owing to the discharge of the fitting itself. Many of the results of this research were given in a paper read before the Institution of Sanitary Engineers by Mr. Wise of the Building Research Station.* Briefly, the findings are that there is little risk of the bath and W.C. traps being unsealed from either cause: the 'trailing discharge' from the flat-bottomed bath – that is, the slow discharge of the last small quantity of water – refilling the trap, even if self-siphonage does take place. A sink, being also a flat-bottomed vessel, has a slow trailing discharge, and thus refills its trap: but a basin, with steeply sloping sides, has no such discharge, and thus self-siphonage may leave the trap with dangerously little water in it.

Whether or not a vent must be used for the basin trap is governed by the length of the waste pipe between fitting trap and stack, and its angle of inclination. Where the distance is no more than 6 in. from trap to stack, the maximum allowable gradient is 20 degrees: but when the distance is 1 ft. 0 in., this has shrunk to 8 degrees, and at 3 ft. 9 in., it is down to 6 degrees. As this is the least gradient for good drainage, it follows that 3 ft. 9 in. from basin outlet to stack is the greatest distance permissible. Thus, the careful planning of the fittings and stack are necessary if the maximum benefit is to be received. Incidentally, there seems no reason why an enterprising manufacturer should not make a basin of a design especially to encourage the trailing discharge: there would be a considerable demand, once its benefits were understood.

13. DRAINS: TRAPS AND SOIL PIPES

In tall buildings using the two-pipe system, practical experience has shown that to eliminate the risk of siphonage, a vent stack for the W.C.s is necessary, but that it can be omitted in the case of the 'waste' fittings, provided only that

* See Bibliography.—Ed.

153

the stack to which the fittings are connected is carried up to form an open vent. Anti-siphon traps may be used but, with the vent as stated, the ordinary deep-seal pattern has proved perfectly successful: nor do they suffer from the gurglings produced by some patterns of re-sealing trap.

Nor would it be inappropriate here to point out the advantages of reducing the number of traps as far as possible in washrooms and the like, where ranges of fittings are installed. As an instance, a separate trap to each of a range of basins connected to a common waste is quite unnecessary: a single trap at the end of the range will suffice. Much of the over-trapping which we see is due to the fear that odour from decaying soap may escape to the room unless a trap is placed immediately next to the fitting; and, indeed, few smells are nastier. The regular use of soapless detergents, however, completely avoids this trouble, and even reduces it once it has started. Finally, the claims of open floor channels with suitable gratings above them, to receive short untrapped branches from the fittings in a washroom, should not be overlooked. The channels discharge to an ordinary trapped gully: in a system recently designed, this is the only trap used to take the wastes from some 18 fittings.

Cast iron, by virtue of its rigidity, cost and resistance to corrosion, remains the most-used soil-pipe material: steel, whilst possessing certain advantages, such as the reduction in the number of joints and ease of jointing and connection to branch pipes, has insufficient resistance to corrosion, unless anti-corrosive treatment is very carefully carried out. In *Post-War Building Studies, No. 26*, the jointing of cast-iron pipes in cement, instead of caulking in lead, is said to be satisfactory; here might be a notable saving in cost.

Copper pipes may be used both for soil and waste pipes, with capillary, compression or welded joints; but in the large sizes the cost is high. The very smooth bore helps to minimize blockages; corrosion is virtually eliminated. Lead, formerly greatly used for soil and waste work, also suffers from high cost: nevertheless, its extreme ease of manipulation renders it ideal for branch connections and the like. It is still good practice to interpose a short length of lead pipe between the W.C. outlet and the soil stack, especially where the W.C. is on a wooden floor, for it permits slight relative movement between bowl and stack without fracture. Lead also lends itself particularly to the forming of the trap vents in a one-pipe system, even where a more rigid material is used for the wastes themselves, and for the main vent stack.

14. PREFABRICATED PLUMBING

The question of prefabrication has been much discussed of recent years – of plumbing, as of all else connected with building. In a scheme of any size, where units are repeated, some prefabrication will almost certainly be worth while, but it is a question of degree. It may mean bringing onto the site complete units, with tanks, heaters, and pipework complete: or it may simply mean the bringing-

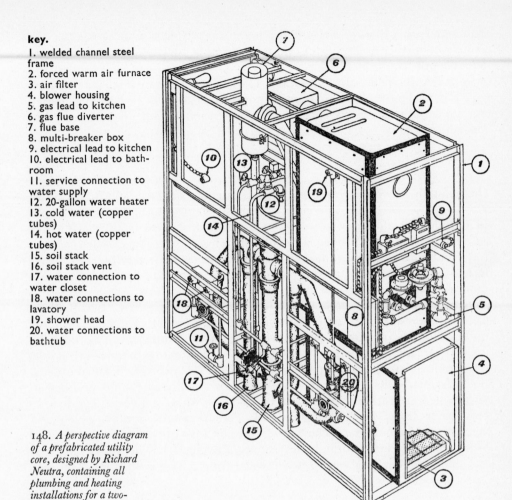

148. *A perspective diagram of a prefabricated utility core, designed by Richard Neutra, containing all plumbing and heating installations for a two-bedroom house.*

on of parts, with some of the manipulation already done. The major argument against the Plumbing Service Unit is that it generally costs more than a similar installation carried out in situ. This is partly because the factory-made article has to carry the factory's overhead costs, as well as the cost of labour and materials; and partly because of heavier transport charges, for the unit when complete is a fragile and bulky article, whilst its individual components are reasonably robust, and readily packed. Also, the unit is inflexible, and it is difficult to make it conform to minor variations in building. For an extensive scheme, partial prefabrication has shown itself to be the most economical, the components being prepared off the site, and finally fitted on it.

There is also much to be said for the use of a site workshop for the preparing of material: this is successfully done in the United States, as well as in this country. A further useful form of prefabrication is the preparation of cast-iron soil and waste stacks for two-storey houses, and their erection as self-supporting units, before the floors are in position. The soil stack is an inconveniently rigid unit, not lending itself in any way to adjustment to suit the building. Better, then, to avoid unnecessary cutting away and making good, by erecting it first and building to it.

15. PIPE DUCTS

The question whether internal soil as well as waste stacks should be permitted is no longer a vexed one. Few now admire the sight of soil pipes draped upon the outside of a building: and with good workmanship no qualms at all need be felt in placing them inside. Although it is comparatively rare in this country, frost conditions do arise sufficiently severe to freeze and possibly to damage outside pipes: the risk is greater with one-pipe systems, where dripping taps may cause a pipe to become frozen, which would not have happened had its contents been only the occasional full-bore discharge from a W.C. In stipulating good workmanship, the architect must assist the plumber by giving him room to work properly: pipe ducts are often designed with insufficient thought on this point. Where planning permits – and usually early attention to the point enables it to be done – it is greatly preferable that stacks, and indeed all plumbing, should be placed in cupboards, where they are readily accessible, and defects quickly obvious, rather than in covered-in ducts, wherein defects may develop to a serious degree before being noticed. The cupboards through which they pass, however, should not include the larder, or any cupboard likely to be used for the storage of food: not only for reasons of hygiene, but because a considerable amount of heat is given off, when water from a bath is discharged through a 4-in. stack.

16. GARBAGE DISPOSAL

The subject of modern drainage methods cannot be left without consideration of garbage disposal. On a high-density site it is always a serious problem, and now it is made the more so by the difficulty of recruiting men for rubbish collection – at no time a pleasant job. Ingenious adaptations of the ordinary rubbish chute have been made, with a view to minimizing handling in multi-storey buildings: but even more ingenious – though, it must be said, a costly example of ingenuity – is the Garchey system of waste disposal. Here, the rubbish is placed in a compartment in a special sink in each flat or dwelling; these sinks are connected, by cast-iron pipes with a minimum diameter of 6 in., to chambers into which the rubbish is flushed. From these chambers, it is drawn by a vacuum pump to a central plant, where it is centrifuged to remove moisture, and burnt, the heat being recovered and made available for water or space heating. For schemes of one hundred units or more, compactly grouped, such a system demands serious consideration in spite of its high capital cost.

Finally, the American Garbage Grinder must be mentioned. This device is also situated beneath the sink, under the fitting and the trap, and consists of rotating grinding plates driven by a small electric motor. Rubbish placed in the machine is ground to sufficiently small size to be flushed by water from the ordinary sink tap down the waste to the ordinary drainage system. A slipping clutch, or similar safety device, protects it from damage in the event of cutlery or similarly indigestible objects finding their way into it: a further safety device prevents its operation until the cover is in position, thus removing any risk to hands. Such devices are used in considerable numbers in the United States, though they are not cheap. They are to some extent frowned upon by sewerage authorities, for the ground product is not readily treated in the sewage works, and their widespread adoption would bring considerable problems in its wake. These problems are not, however, insoluble, and the undoubted convenience of such devices makes the solution of the problems involved worth while.

17. UNDERGROUND DRAINAGE SYSTEMS

Of underground drainage systems, there is little to be said: even in the United States, home of many ingenious ideas and new materials, many drainage engineers prefer good glazed stoneware pipes to other materials, and in this country, except for very large sizes where concrete is used, their use is almost universal. Suggestions are made in *Post-War Building Studies, No. 26*, that some saving in cost should be made by a reduction in the number of inspection chambers; these being placed at changes of direction of the drains alone, whilst branch connections were made with ordinary Y junctions. It is properly pointed out that chambers are not only a convenient means of clearing drains, but of blocking them as well: a readily lifted cover is a convenient means of disposing of waste. The suggestion is that accurate plans would make easy the finding of a Y junction for clearance purposes, in the very unlikely event of its becoming blocked. Experience shows, however, that such plans tend to disappear; and, memories being short, considerable excavation – and damage to gardens and roads – might have to be done to find the site of the blockage.

Rapid and complete methods of clearing obstructions from drains are of great importance in maintaining sanitary conditions. Also, they have their influence on the actual design of the systems, for it is important to design them to enable them easily to be cleared, within the limits of the clearing equipment available. In most cases, in this country, this means ordinary cane rods; and as long as this is so, the normal bye-law requirement of 300 feet between inspection chambers is a fair one. At the best, hand-operated drain machines are to be found. In America, however, the use of power-driven clearing equipment enables a drain to be cleared for a considerably greater distance from an access and, as a result, where such equipment is available, chambers are placed up to 500 feet apart on straight runs, with consequent economy, especially where drains run deep, and chambers have to be correspondingly large.

The use of pitch-fibre pipes, fairly commonly used in the United States and Canada, deserves comment. These make a useful alternative to the more conventional materials used for underground drainage; their major advantage is extreme speed of laying, pipes being 8–12 ft. long, and having a simple spigot and socket joint which, by nature of the material, needs no jointing or preparation; the two pipes are merely forced together as Fig. 126, page 138, indicates. Ease of transport is a further advantage. Such pipes are now available in this country.

Modern sanitary practice has compassed the demise of yet another trap – this time, the interceptor. In time past, when gases from the drains were thought to be a cause of many a disease, it was clearly a good policy to keep them as far from the building as possible. Now, medical science has shown that these gases are less lethal than was formerly supposed, and in dilute form they can be loosed from the vent stacks of buildings without causing illness or even nuisance. Good ventilation is a most desirable end in all drainage work; by omitting the interceptor, each vent stack becomes a sewer vent, and this end is secured. Further, the omission of the interceptor eliminates one of the most vulnerable parts of a drainage system, from the point of view of obstruction: and it also eliminates that most tiresome concomitant, the fresh air inlet; all too often, the derangement of the flap means that it acts rather as a bad smell outlet than as a fresh air inlet. Interceptors are still demanded in some districts – as, indeed, are outside soil pipes – but the number is constantly shrinking.

18. PLANNING: THE CLOSET

Now, finally, we come to the planning of those parts of a house which affect, and are affected by, the sanitary installation. In the first place, the water closet. It must be obvious that, except perhaps in the case of the smallest flat, a W.C. must be provided which is not in a bathroom, to which access may be denied to others by prolonged occupation by a bather; but where more than one W.C. is provided, it is good practice to place the second – usually the upstairs – one, in the bathroom: for by so doing, the cleanly habit of washing after its use is encouraged. In the case of a separate downstairs closet, the addition of a washbasin, however small, is desirable. The placing of the water closet in the bathroom frequently simplifies the connections to the single stack of a one-pipe system: generally, also, it saves space. In the United States, this has been taken a step further: complete units are available, comprising bath, basin, and W.C., of very ingenious and clean design: though one cannot but wonder if breakage of some part might not lead to excessive cost of replacement.

The bye-law air brick is a far from satisfactory ventilating device for the W.C.: all too often the air current is inwards, and smells are carried into the house. A new device sets out to eliminate this trouble: a small extract fan is arranged to operate during the period of the refilling of the cistern.

19. PLANNING: THE KITCHEN

The planning of kitchens is a much more complex subject. There can scarcely be fewer ideas on what is a well-planned domestic kitchen than there are house-wives. Trite sayings there have been: 'The kitchen is the workshop of the house' and the like. In fact, far more often, if industrial analogy is needed, it is the workshop, manager's office, and canteen rolled into one. It is possible to segregate the various activities which may take place in the kitchen and its ancillaries; but it is not necessarily desirable to do so. The tendency now is to divide the kitchen area into working kitchen, utility room, and eating space.

Restrictions on floor area, and cost, preclude any of these being of greater than the minimum size. The question must be, then, whether – in place of a number of cramped little spaces, each devoted to a particular purpose or group of purposes – it would not be preferable to adopt that which is already fashion-able for the 'front of the house' – open planning: in fact, a new version of the old farmhouse kitchen. By all means, let us plan that part of the kitchen in which the actual cooking takes place, to spare the housewife's steps, and to give a logical sequence of actions: but let this form part of a larger and wider room.

Modern equipment has made this possible. For instance, the utility room, modern counterpart of the old wash-house, has laundering as its main activity. When washing implied clouds of steam from old-fashioned coppers or wash-boilers, there was everything to be said for keeping it out of the kitchen: but the modern washing machine is virtually steamless. Nor should drying take place even in the utility room: the provision of a proper drying closet, with heat-ing and, above all, good ventilation – or in a flat, where space for this does not exist, a ready-made drying cupboard – is the proper answer to this problem.

Again, to eat in the kitchen may, in the minds of some, imply a scent of frying clinging to the clothes, long after meal. But here, a carefully designed hood over the cooker, with extract fan, can eliminate this unpleasant effect. Such a fan has also the merit of keeping smells out of the rest of the house, by ensur-ing that the air in the kitchen is at a slightly lower pressure, so that draughts are always into, and not out of, it.

The presence of sinks in the kitchen, in which meals are eaten, has been pro-nounced undesirable: and indeed a pile of unwashed plates and dishes standing on the draining board is not a sight to encourage the appetite. But this is a difficulty easily overcome: a sufficient number of adequately large sinks, with movable covers, enables used utensils to be placed in one, covered, and left unseen to soak; and this greatly aids their subsequent washing. A separate sink for clothes-washing is a real advantage; the washing machine should be near it.

It is particularly desirable for solid-fuel cookers to be installed in kitchens of sufficient size. Even the best insulated of them give off a considerable amount of heat. Installed in small rooms, they overheat them: a window is flung open, and the valuable heat, paid for at considerable expense, is dissipated. On the other hand, many give off just enough heat to keep comfortably warm a kitchen of perhaps 200 square feet, without resorting to radiators or other heating system. With gas or electric cookers, insufficient heat is given off, even for a small kitchen; auxiliary heating apparatus is in any case needed. A gas cooker may release an excess of moisture which, by virtue of its greater concentration, is the more objectionable in a small kitchen than in a large; although the extract fan already mentioned will reduce the unpleasant effects of condensation. A large refrigerator gives off a very appreciable amount of heat: this heat need not be wasted, for if the machine is placed in the kitchen, it will be usefully employed in helping to warm it. Incidentally, few pieces of domestic equipment are more valuable than the deep-freeze refrigerator, in which foods can be stored for many months, and tough old birds made tender. Certain types, of table-top height, are particularly to be commended, as they add to, rather than detract from, the working space in the kitchen.

Of kitchen furniture, a large number of standardized designs are available, varying from the cheapest wooden types to the most costly enamelled metal. As with most things, one gets what one pays for; but even the wooden utility units, when obtained from a reliable manufacturer, are quite satisfactory, and give the opportunity of building up commodious furniture, of good appearance, at a reasonable price. Of the dearer types, one particularly complete example even includes the domestic boiler within a unit matching the rest. Such units make much easier the task of the kitchen planner; there is little reason for the use of purpose-made units save in exceptional cases.

This short survey can give no more than an impression of the trends in sanitation, hygiene and allied subjects in modern building: in this, as in all other fields, research continues, and improvements are constantly made. If this chapter has done nothing else but to whet the reader's appetite for greater knowledge, it will have served a useful purpose: and to help him, a bibliography is appended.

BIBLIOGRAPHY

Building Drainage. (Code of Practice, C.P. 301, 1950. British Standards Institution.)

Domestic Drainage. (Post-War Building Study, No. 26. H.M.S.O., 1947.)

Drainage for Housing. Digest No. 55. (Building Research Station, June, 1953.)

Electrolytic Protection. H. G. Goddard, M.A., F.R.I.B.A. (Architects' Journal, December 21, 1950.)

Improvements in Systems of 'Combined' Sewerage. R. C. Carter, F.R.San.I. (Paper presented to the Institution of Sanitary Engineers, December 13, 1949.)

Lead Alloy Pipe: Silver – Copper – Lead. Lead Industries Development Council Bulletin, No. 114. (Lead Industries Council, Jermyn Street, S.W.1.)

Lead and Lead Alloy Water Service Pipe below ground. Lead Industries Development Council Bulletin, No. 112. (Lead Industries Council, Jermyn Street, S.W.1.)

One-Pipe Plumbing – Some recent Experimental Hydraulics at the Building Research Station. A. F. E. Wise, M.Sc. (Paper read to the Institution of Sanitary Engineers, November 22, 1951.)

One-Pipe (Single-Stack) Plumbing for Housing. Digest, No. 48. (Building Research Station, November, 1952.)

One-Pipe (Single-Stack) Plumbing for Housing. Part II, Principles of Design. Digest No. 49. (Building Research Station, December, 1952.)

Plumbing. (Post-War Building Study, No. 4. H.M.S.O., 1944.)

Plumbing in America. (National Building Study: Special Report, No. 2. Building Research Station. H.M.S.O., 1948.)

The Purification of Water Supplies. G. Bransby-Williams. Chapman & Hall, 1946. Out of print.

Reinforced Lead Pipes. (Report of the Institution of Water Engineers' Research Group, presented to the Institution, December 7, 1951. Reported in The Surveyor, December 15, 1951.)

Sanitary Services – Their Effect on the Design and Planning of Buildings. F. L. Barrow, M.Sc., A.M.I.C.E. (Paper read to the R.I.B.A., November 21, 1950.)

Self-Siphonage of Fixture Traps. (United States Department of Commerce: National Bureau of Standards. Building Materials and Structures Report, 126. U.S. Government Printing Office, Washington 25, D.C., 1951.)

The Use of Copper and Galvanized Steel in the Same Hot-Water System. Digest, No. 8. (Building Research Station, July, 1949.)

Water Softening. (Report of the Water-Softening Sub-Committee of the Central Advisory Water Committee. H.M.S.O., 1944.)

INTERIOR FINISHES *Kenneth Cheesman*

1. INTRODUCTION

Every year conditions in relation to building change, owing to a variety of causes, the majority of which are in one way or another the result of current economic changes. The annual budget, international markets and controls, are only a few of the factors which constantly react on the cost of basic materials; and wage rates, tied as they are to the cost of living, add their heavy weight to the final cost of building and interior work.

So violent is the effect of these factors from time to time, that the use of some key material may be virtually prohibited, keeping research departments busy finding substitutes at short notice, and designers constantly on their toes evolving novel methods of construction to cope with the particular form of frustration encountered.

If architects and designers are to survive these difficult periods, it is essential for them to keep up-to-date, as far as possible, with the rapid changes which constantly influence their specifications, since so few practising in Great Britain to-day are still at liberty to use materials regardless of cost.

During periods of rapidly rising cost, it frequently occurs that delays caused by licensing and other authorities result in earlier estimates being so exceeded that drastic cuts have to be made at a stage when it is too late to alter the structural programme. The inevitable result is that a vicious attack is made on the interior finishes, and it is here that the widest knowledge of the possibilities offered by relatively cheap material can save the situation.

In this section, under broad headings such as Floors, Ceilings, and so on it is intended to draw attention to the most valuable of recent developments and inventions which have been evolved to assist the harassed designer in his endless battle against unpredictable hazards, whatever form they may take.

2. FLOOR FINISHES

Under the above general heading the principal types will be classified alphabetically – reference to individual trade names being made only when unique claims or advantages are considered worthy of special mention.

A brief description of each type will include particulars of any outstanding features whether advantages or disadvantages – suitability to special purposes, a rough cost-figure per square yard laid, and any other facts which should be of interest, or assist a designer in deciding the most suitable finish for his purpose.

It must be clearly understood that cost-figures quoted here cannot be regarded as stable, since all the factors affecting them are constantly fluctuating, and because the figure includes laying, involving labour costs, travelling time, and expenses, it will vary appreciably in different parts of the country.

They have, however, all been based on manufacturers' figures given at the same time, fixing being assumed to be in London, and they will consequently serve as a comparative indication of the general price level of one type in relation to another.

Because, in the majority of cases, no floor surface can be expected to give satisfactory service unless it is applied to a wholly satisfactory sub-floor, manufacturers' specifications or recommendations on this subject are particularly stressed.

Asphalt (jointless floors)

Obtainable from 11s. to 12s. per square yard, laid, in black only. A variety of subdued colours can be supplied – red, fawn, grey, green and blue, but these vary considerably in cost from 15s. to 35s. in accordance with the special pigments required.

A variable proportion of grit, or fine granite chippings is included as an aggregate – the amount being increased for heavier floors. Principal advantages are its *low cost* and the fact that it is *absolutely waterproof*.

It is laid direct on concrete by asphalt specialists, saving the cost of a cement screed.

It is an advantage, however, to provide an insulation membrane of sheeting felt directly on the concrete, at an extra cost of 10d. per yard, before the asphalt is laid.

An acid-resisting asphalt can be supplied for battery rooms or other special purpose floors.

Jointless asphalt floors are particularly suitable for markets, lavatories, factories or kitchens, where it is an advantage to be able to hose down a floor frequently. In such cases, the floor should be turned up to form a deep cove at all walls, and be laid to a fall in accordance with the drainage system.

Concrete Tiles (pre-cast)

Obtainable from 28s. per square yard laid, in a considerable range of colours (red, orange, buff, light and dark brown, grey, black, and white), in standard sizes 6×6 in., 8×8 in., 9×9 in., 10×10 in., by approximately ¾ in., and 12×12 in. by 1 in. thick.

Colour is introduced only into the wearing surface which is approximately one-third the total thickness. The remaining two-thirds consists of a plain concrete backing.

Green and blue can also be supplied, but cost rather more because of the pigments required. Some manufacturers will also make especially to colour-samples at around 30s. per yard.

A non-slip variety is available, ribbed diagonally, and it is also possible for carborundum to be incorporated in the tile, if required.

Specially suited to railway stations, booking halls, canteens, kitchens, school cloakrooms, and where subject to severe pedestrian traffic. Pre-cast concrete tiles are, however, *not* suitable for external use.

Cork Tiles

Obtainable from 35s. to 40s. per square yard laid, in standard sizes 6×6 in., 9×9 in., 12×12 in., 9×3 in. and 12×4 in. – in thicknesses of from $\frac{1}{4}$ in. to $\frac{9}{16}$ in.

Colour is strictly limited to that of natural cork, the only choice being three tones, light, medium and rich dark brown.

Tiles are laid direct to wood-floated cement screed by means of a bitumen-type mastic, but are sometimes fixed with special case-hardened steel pins which can be driven into the screed.

There is no warmer floor material than compressed cork tiles, and in addition, they provide an extremely quiet and comfortable floor, capable of taking and retaining a high degree of polish without being slippery.

They are consequently most suitable for public libraries, hospitals, board rooms and offices, and their comfort and warmth are of special value on bathroom floors.

Cork Carpet

Obtainable in sheet form at about 25s. 6d. per square yard laid, cork carpet is superior, although very similar in appearance, to linoleum. It can be supplied in much the same colour range as lino, but being of cork composition, it offers the advantages of that material – greater warmth, silence, and comfort.

It is usually of slightly thicker substance than lino, $\frac{1}{8}$ – $\frac{3}{16}$ in. Fixing methods and sub-floor specification are similar to those given under the heading of Linoleum.

Composition Floors (jointless), (see also Asphalt, Magnesite and Semastic)

This heading includes flooring materials composed from a variety of bases, such as asphalt, asbestos, or latex, with other components each contributing some functional part in the final product. The usual combination is a base, a filler and a bond.

As a result of such a variety of ingredients, these floors, under their respective trade names, offer a variety of qualities and their suitability to different types

164

of building depends on the degree of durability, flexibility, cheapness, hardness or warmth which they have to offer.

Prices range from 12*s.* to 20*s.* per square yard laid.

Composition Floors (*pre-cast*) *Tiles*
Obtainable from 12*s.* to 20*s.* per square yard laid, in a reasonably good range of plain colours, and also in marbled effects, preferred by many clients on account of the figure's helping to camouflage marks and stains from wear.

When selecting these, architects should ensure that the veining runs right through – otherwise, if it is only on the surface, it may quickly disappear in parts where wear is heavy.

Pre-cast composition tiles can as a rule be laid direct on 'ruled' concrete, thus saving the cost of screeding.

Granolithic Floors (*jointless*)
Granolithic finish consists of cement with fine granite chips, and is obtainable in its natural cement colour from about 10*s.* 6*d.* per square yard laid. It can also be supplied with the addition of colouring pigment in green, blue-grey, and a dull red, at slight extra cost.

It should be stressed, however, that a granolithic finish is apt not to bond with the concrete sub-floor unless laid while the concrete is still wet.

Carborundum can be incorporated in the surface if a particularly non-slip finish is necessary.

Hard wear is sometimes inclined to cause 'dusting' and in kitchens where this would be particularly objectionable, it can be effectively remedied by treating with a solution of one part (by volume) of silicate of soda and three parts of warm water.

Industrial Floors
A large variety of floor finishes are available for industrial purposes, from light surfaces to reinforced heavy-duty floors at costs varying from 30*s.* to £3 per square yard laid.

The heavier varieties only will be dealt with here, the lighter types being included under their appropriate headings.

The various forms include cast-iron grid and steel chequer plates in standard units of 6 × 12 in., and 12 × 12 in., and a number of composition types armoured by means of honeycomb and other patent steel reinforcement, capable of withstanding the traffic of heavy wheeled trucks.

Magnesite Flooring (*jointless, and pre-cast tiles*)
This is a flooring of comparatively recent introduction.

Manufactured to a British Standard Specification it consists of a magnesium chloride base, a wood-flour filler, and a bonding agent.

Broadly speaking, the product is of an asbestos nature, and it is obtainable in standard pre-cast tiles in a good range of plain colours, and also in marbled effects at about 20s. per yard laid.

As with terrazzo floors, manufacturers recommend the use of pre-cast tiles as the only guarantee against the subsequent cracking of the hard surface as a result of air or water cavities. This floor can roughly be regarded as at the low-cost end of the hard floor scale, with pre-cast terrazzo tiles at the luxury end.

Tiles are laid direct to 'ruled' concrete, saving the cost of cement screed.

Linoleum

Little description is necessary of a material so extensively used as linoleum, but there are a number of points concerning fixing which are not generally appreciated, or about which conflicting opinions are sometimes expressed.

It is occasionally said that dry rot can be caused through mastic-fixed lino's excluding air from the wood sub-floor. This is not true, for, whilst dampness and lack of ventilation encourage dry rot which already exists, practical experience shows that there is no great danger of dry rot's resulting from complete coverage.

Almost any recognized linoleum adhesive can be used, and in the majority of cases, where movement in the sub-floor is not likely to be great, the use of a dry felt underlay paper, laid crosswise to the boards, is recommended, and the underlay should be bonded both to the floor and the linoleum.

Where movement is expected to be considerable owing to changes of temperature or intermittent heating, or where there is a possibility of damp, it is advisable to lay the lino loose.

It is inadvisable to lay lino on wood which has been treated with creosote or similar oily preparations.

On New Wood Floors. For ideal conditions, boards should be well seasoned and of not more than 4 in. width because of the tendency to curl causing ridges in line. Adequate ventilation must be provided below joist level, with damp-proof course on all walls. The lino should be allowed to lie for a day or two before it is cut to fit.

On Old Wood Floors. Care must be taken to remove or drive home all nails, tacks, etc. and any loose boards must be made firm. The problem is entirely one of providing an adequately smooth, even surface, and where roughness is the result of uneven shrinkage of boards, felt paper is of little use. Depressions can be filled by means of a suitable plastic filler, and high spots smoothed down with a rasp, plane, or if available, a sanding machine.

In extreme cases where a first-class finish is insisted upon, an all-over screed of sand, cement and latex, or sand, cement and bitumen can be applied. This need not add much more than the difference between the highest and lowest points in the surface, $\frac{1}{8} - \frac{3}{16}$ in.

On New Concrete. Sub-floor should finish with not less than $\frac{3}{4}$-in. screed consisting of 1 part cement to 2 parts screened sand, levelled and finished with wood float.

Expansion joints left in the concrete should be filled level with the top surface. Concrete must be allowed to dry out before lino is laid.

If lino is to be laid with adhesive and concrete is 'dusting', a dressing of 1 part (by volume) of silicate of soda to 3 parts of warm water, brushed over, should remedy it, provided 24 hours are allowed for drying out before laying the linoleum.

On Old Concrete. Attention must be paid to improving as much as possible any roughness in the surface and cleaning out loose dirt from cracks or expansion joints, and filling level with a plastic filler.

On Damp Concrete. Concrete floors in a basement or on ground level must have a substantial damp-proof course to prevent damp from rising. If no such provision exists the only solution is to lay a bed of $\frac{3}{4}$-in. rock asphalt in two layers, or three-ply composite bitumen damp-proof course, on top.

If this is not done, the damp will rise by capillary attraction through the concrete, causing deterioration of the adhesive, and may eventually cause the lino to rot.

Marble

Owing to the exceedingly high cost of marble at the present time, which may be quoted as varying from £4 to £8 per square yard laid, it can be expected to play only a very minor part in the finishes specified by interior designers in this country.

It is one of our misfortunes that we should be deprived of the use of a natural material of such dignity and individuality as marble, but owing to the fact that 80 per cent of it is imported from the Continent, it is clear that we shall have to get on without it for quite a number of years.

It is, nevertheless, still used in some of the better-class shop fronts and entrances, and an interesting development has only comparatively recently come to this country from Italy in the form of random broken marble flooring, which is useful in design on account of the rugged texture it provides, and the variety of scale to which it can be applied (Fig. 156, p. 179).

Parquet (and Wood Block Floors)

Obtainable from 40s. to 45s. per sq. yd. laid in the characteristic herringbone or alternative simple patterns. Extensively used before the war, parquet flooring must now be regarded as a luxury finish on account of its high cost. It is nevertheless still considered one of the most satisfactory floors for better-class domestic and commercial use – one of its greatest advantages being that, no matter how badly it has been treated, re-surfacing is a comparatively simple and inexpensive process by means of a sanding machine.

This can be a valuable asset in galleries, showrooms and premises which are likely to change hands periodically.

Laid in bitumen on cement screed, the blocks are usually $\frac{3}{4}$ – 1 in. thick.

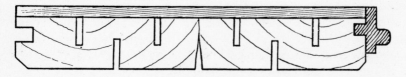

149. *Section through a piece of patent laminated parquet or strip flooring now mass produced in Sweden and available in this country. The invention was made by Gustav Kähr the idea being to combine a hardwood wearing-surface with a supporting structure of cheaper softwood, to form a non-warping, non-swelling, non-shrinking floorboard that can be handled as easily as an ordinary softwood tongued and grooved board, and does not require any sub-flooring. (Masters and Andren Ltd.)*

Plywood

Plywood squares were extensively used before the war and it is difficult to find a warmer or more pleasing effect when it is available. It is unsuitable for anything but light wear: as if heavy traffic is concentrated in any one spot, the surface 'ply' is apt to be worn away altogether, exposing the bond.

Being comparatively thin, it was effectively used in conversions for re-surfacing old floors where the boards had shrunk, leaving wide gaps.

When obtainable, standard size squares in ash or oak 9 × 9 in., 12 × 12 in., or 18 × 18 in., can be supplied, pinned to timber sub-floors, stopped, and polished from 30s. per sq. yd.

P.V.C.

P.V.C. (Poly-vinyl-chloride) is a synthetic, rubber-like product obtainable for floors in both sheet and tile form, approximately $\frac{1}{8}$-in thick from 20s. to 35s. per sq. yd. laid.

It is available in a considerable variety of plain colours, which are remarkable for their purity and brilliance. No other material, except rubber, is able to touch it where yellow, orange, bright blues and similar pure colours are required.

Its main advantage is its extreme toughness and flexibility. It is completely acid-resisting, and as a result of this it is particularly applicable to public houses, milk bars and similar interiors.

Laying is by means of special adhesives recommended by the manufacturers, and it is essential that cement screed is level and steel-trowel finished – the more normal wood float finish being insufficiently smooth. It can also be laid on a wood sub-floor providing irregularities in boarding have been smoothed out.

P.V.C. Safety Flooring

Certain P.V.C. flooring (under the name of Altro Safety Flooring) has incorporated in it Aluminium Oxide abrasive which has the effect of making it permanently non-slip whether wet or dry. It can be supplied in two thicknesses, 2.5 mm. and 4 mm., either in rolls 36 in. wide and 25–30 ft. long, or in 12 × 12 in. or 9 × 9 in. tiles – approximate cost 38s. to 45s. per sq. yd. laid.

Having a hessian base, this material is easily stuck to wood or concrete with any good flooring adhesive.

Coved skirting and stair nosings with rounded edges are also available.

Quarry Tiles

An extremely hardwearing and comparatively inexpensive finish obtainable in standard sizes 6 × 6 in. and 9 × 9 in. by 1 in. thick from 24s. to 32s. per sq. yd. laid.

Colour is limited to a brick red and a blue grey.

Standard tiles have a smooth face but a special non-slip type is available, deeply ribbed diagonally.

Quarry tiles are acid-resisting and consequently suitable for battery rooms, and similar special purposes, but it is necessary to stress the point that the normal bedding cement on which they would be laid is *not* acid-resisting, and unless an acid-resisting jointing material is used, the problem will merely be transferred to finding an acid-resisting bed.

Much used for canteens, kitchens, etc. on account of their durability and smooth and easily cleaned surface, they are inclined to be somewhat noisy, and hard and cold to the feet.

They are normally laid in cement to cement-screeded concrete.

Hard tiles of similar nature are also available in a purplish brown.

Rubber Flooring (Sheet and Tiles)

Obtainable in a large variety of clean plain colours and with marbled effects in sheeting 6 ft. wide or in standard tile from 6 × 6 in., 9 × 9 in., 12 × 12 in. by $\frac{1}{8}-\frac{1}{4}$ in. thick, from 30s. per sq. yd. laid.

The natural qualities of rubber make it especially suited to situations where silence, tough wearing and a hygienic floor covering have to be combined. It is suitable for homes, hospitals, cinemas, etc., staircases and public corridors in ships.

Laid direct to *steel*-trowelled cement screed by means of special rubber adhesives recommended by the manufacturers.

Semastic Tiles – See Thermoplastic Tiles

Terrazzo (in Situ, Jointless Floors)

Broadly speaking Terrazzo is a smooth, hard-wearing finish composed of marble chippings of various grades, from fine to coarse, bonded by cement.

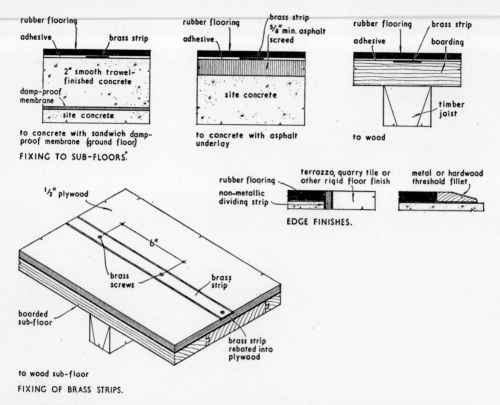

FIXING TO SUB-FLOORS.

rubber flooring
adhesive
brass strip
2" smooth trowel-finished concrete
damp-proof membrane
site concrete
to concrete with sandwich damp-proof membrane (ground floor)

rubber flooring
brass strip
⅝" min. asphalt screed
adhesive
site concrete
to concrete with asphalt underlay

rubber flooring
brass strip
adhesive
boarding
timber joint
to wood

EDGE FINISHES.

rubber flooring
terrazzo, quarry tile or other rigid floor finish
non-metallic dividing strip
metal or hardwood threshold fillet

FIXING OF BRASS STRIPS.

½" plywood
6"
brass screws
brass strip
boarded sub-floor
brass strip rebated into plywood
to wood sub-floor

150. *Rubber flooring in operating theatres must be anti-static because a discharge of static electricity might cause sparks which could ignite the inflammable anaesthetic gases. These diagrams show methods of conducting the electricity away by brass earthing strips 1 in. wide by 5/1,000 or 10/1,000 in. thick laid not more than 4 ft. apart and running to a suitable earthing point such as a water pipe. (Semtex Ltd.)*

It is spread on a concrete sub-floor in plastic form, and when dry is ground and polished to form a smooth jointless surface of first-class quality. It may be turned up to form a cove at junctions with walls, and be used as a finish for both treads and risers of staircases.

Suppliers strongly advocate wherever possible the use of pre-cast tiles for flooring, because of the probability of a jointless floor cracking before long as a result of the formation of air or water cavities during the process of laying.

Terrazzo (Pre-cast Tiles)

Are obtainable in standard sizes 6×6 in., 9×9 in., and 12×12 in., in a variety of pale tints, and grades of fine or coarse marble aggregate.

The extra cost of laying tiles is in the region of 2s. 6d. per sq. yd. and they are fixed direct to cement-screeded concrete with cement.

It is considered an advantage to insulate the tiles from the sub-floor by means of a membrane of sheeting-felt, and in cases where there is liable to be movement in the sub-floor, the tiles have been laid on a bed of compressed sand contained between two sheets of waterproof paper.

Pre-cast Terrazzo tiles may be regarded as a first-class floor finish for hospitals, entrance halls, canteens, kitchens, and similar places where its easily-washable hard surface and durability justify the initial high cost.

Thermoplastic (pre-cast tiles)

Thermoplastic tiles are one of the more recent floor finishes manufactured to an American Standard Specification. They are a combination of a number of components – usually a base, colour pigments, and a bonding agent.

They are supplied under a variety of trade names in a reasonably good range of standard colours, and the usual size is 9×9 in. The standard thickness is about $\frac{3}{16}$ in.

The sub-floor requires to be dead level and must be steel-trowel finished, and it must be understood from the beginning that the fixing of all thermoplastic tiles is a specialist tile-fixer's job, since the process of laying involves heating the tiles until they reach the correct degree of flexibility for laying.

The great popularity of this finish is owing to its low cost ($23s. – 35s.$ per sq. yd. laid), especially where really large areas are to be covered. It is almost universally applied in offices, and circulation areas of administrative buildings, factories and industrial premises of all kinds where a hygienic and economic floor is required. It is also being used on a considerable scale for schools and housing (as a finish for living-room floors).

Vitreous Tile and Mosaic

Tiles are hard with a vitreous finish on the face. Supplied in standard sizes of 4×4 in. and 6×6 in. they offer a good range of pale colours, and being non-porous are well suited to such work as lavatories, cloak rooms, bathrooms and kitchens. Average cost runs about $60s.$ per sq. yd. fixed, but special colours, or special sizes are apt to cost considerably more. Cove sections, cappings and internal and external angles are also standardized.

Non-Slip tiles are also produced, some with ribbed surfaces and others in which carborundum is incorporated in the body.

Wood Blocks (see also Parquet)

In addition to parquet floors there are a number of other wood-block floor finishes available in different thicknesses and sizes, the majority of which can be laid direct to concrete with a bitumen-type mastic.

Wood Mosaic

Thinner and smaller blocks are often referred to as Wood Mosaic.

Wood Strip Floors

Wherever a dance-floor is required, this is the best type to specify. The ideal wood for the purpose – Canadian white maple – coming from a hard-currency country, is no longer an economical proposition. The most used substitutes are European beech – approximately 44*s*. per sq. yd. laid; East African poliondo – approximately 48*s*. per sq. yd. laid; Nigerian danta – approximately 45*s*. per sq. yd. laid; and Japanese maple – approximately 48*s*. per sq. yd. laid.

The method of laying is usually by secret nailing to suspended joists or to wood fillets inserted into the sub-floor at approximately 14-18 in. centres.

A patent wood-strip floor which has comparatively recently appeared on the market is of Swedish origin, and consists of softwood boards slotted lengthwise alternately on the top side and under side, with a relatively thin facing of hardwood units approximately $4\frac{1}{2} \times 1\frac{1}{2}$ in. running crosswise (Fig. 149, p. 168).

Carpet, Haircord and Matting

Although the above floor coverings are generally regarded as furnishing materials, it seems wrong to give all available information regarding linoleum and to withhold it in the case of these infinitely more comfortable and attractive materials.

Carpet. In addition to the normal width of 27 in., standard plain carpets, and the larger-scale figured carpets are frequently available in a 36 in. width, but the standard 27 in. is cheaper *pro rata* than other widths.

A few of the more progressive manufacturers are now able to supply seamless carpets (to order) up to 15 ft. by almost any length, and in one instance up to 33 ft. in width – the length being governed only by the problem of transport to the site and handling.

There are a number of officially classified grades of quality from W.O. which is the best, down to W.5 which is the cheapest. The difference in quality is almost directly related to the number of tufts to the square inch and the depth of the pile.

Whilst the current price of carpets is continually changing, comparative prices for the various grades are all that can be quoted here. At the present time when W.O. quality is 94*s*. 3*d*. per yard (27 in. wide) W.5. quality is 33*s*. 3*d*.

A good quality underfelt, which is essential whatever the sub-floor may be, costs on the same comparative basis, 8*s*. 6*d*. per yard (54 in. wide), and for the work of measuring, making and laying, a further 5*s*. per yard for the carpet, and 1*s*. per yard for the underfelt, should be allowed.

Hair-Cord. As its name suggests, this is woven from a mixture of hair, jute and wool. It is available in a somewhat limited selection of colours, natural, grey, green, blue, rust and fawn – and is sold at from 20*s*. to 30*s*. per yard in standard 27 in. width. It can also be obtained in 36 in. width.

Heavy Felt. Substantial felt floor coverings from $\frac{1}{8}$ in. to nearly $\frac{3}{8}$ in. thick, 48–50 in. wide, are obtainable in a fairly comprehensive range of subdued plain colours – prices varying from 30s. per yard to 45s. One or two felt and carpet manufacturers can offer material which they guarantee 'mothproof' and it is as well to stipulate this in any specification.

Rubber-backed Needleloom Felt. This is a comparatively new floor material consisting of a needled felt surface on a rubber base. It is manufactured in a range of fairly subdued colours and sells at 12s. to 16s. per square yard. Its rubber back gives it an additional advantage, enabling it to remain in position when used as a loose mat on polished floors of all descriptions. Almost all other materials would slip.

Sisal Matting. Very good quality, tough-wearing woven sisal matting is available in a number of standard patterns and colours, and this can be supplied in widths of 3 ft., 4½ ft., 6 ft., and 9 ft., at 25s. per square yard.

When cut this matting very quickly frays, and manufacturers will usually make up any required shape or size, cutting and binding edges with tape to match the colour of the matting at a very reasonable additional cost.

Coconut Fibre Matting. This is in most respects similar to sisal matting but somewhat cheaper and varying from 12s. 6d. to 16s. per sq. yard. Owing to the natural fibre being a stronger brown colour, the colour range in this matting is more limited and more subdued than in sisal matting.

Hand-woven Rush Matting. This material is obtainable in its natural colour, and is available in 36 in. and 72 in. widths at approximately 32s. 6d. per sq. yd. It is suitable for garden rooms, sun lounges, roof gardens and loggias, and can sometimes be effectively introduced into halls, passages, landings and even dining rooms.

Laying. Carpets are fixed to wood floors by nailing, but on hard floors such as cement, asphalt or composition, there are two methods of fixing commonly employed.

On new work provision should be made by letting in wood strips – ½ in. deep and 1½ in. wide, to finish flush with the sub-floor – all round the walls, and, if the room is large, it is advisable to introduce similar fixing strips in one direction only (across the narrower width) at say 10–12 ft. intervals.

On old work, where no provision has been made, it is necessary to have holes (approximately 1 in. diameter or a little larger) drilled at 6 in. to 9 in. intervals all round the walls, and filled up flush with lead. The carpet is then nailed into these lead plugs.

3. CEILING- AND WALL-BOARDS

It is only within the scope of this section to consider various types of ceiling and wallboards which can either be regarded as a finish in themselves, or as a suitable base for an applied finish such as paint or wall-paper.*

* Though coming, perhaps, as much under the scope of structure as of finishes, an interesting new type of ceiling should be mentioned here in passing. This is the 'Meta-Mica' reinforced

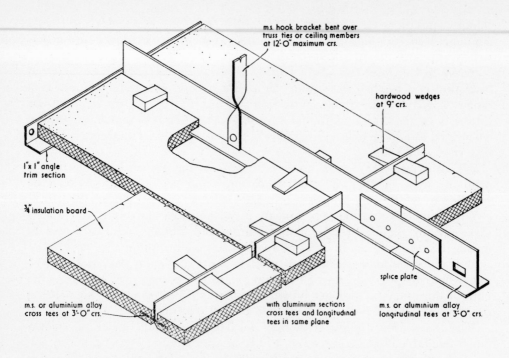

m.s. hook bracket bent over
truss ties or ceiling members
at 12'-0" maximum crs.

hardwood wedges
at 9" crs.

1"x 1" angle
trim section

¾" insulation board

splice plate

m.s. or aluminium alloy
cross tees at 3'-0" crs.

with aluminium sections
cross tees and longitudinal
tees in same plane

m.s. or aluminium alloy
longitudinal tees at 3'-0" crs.

151. *An invisible method of fixing building boards for suspended ceilings in which all fixing members are concealed behind the ceiling face. Suspension and jointing members are of mild steel or aluminium alloy T-sections. The lower edges of the panels are chamfered and all that is seen from below is the surface of the boards with V-joints. (Anderson Construction Co.)*

In regard to ceiling boards, numerous patent methods of fixing have been devised and are recommended by individual manufacturers for their own products. Most of these consist basically of as economical a skeleton structure as possible, to members of which the ceiling-board units can be nailed or fastened with clips ingeniously designed to facilitate quick erection.

A typical example is illustrated in diagram form (Fig. 151).

For fixing wallboards, it will be obvious that the spacing of rough grounds, studding or independent framing, to support the different types, will vary with the thickness and rigidity of the particular board, from something like 3 ft. centres with the thicker blockboards, to 16 in. centres in the case of thin ply or hardboard. Such grounds may run either vertically or horizontally – cross

vermiculite panel originally designed for the Ministry of Education Architectural Department, who wanted a thermal insulating, fire-proof, secretly fixed, sound-absorbent and decorative ceiling panel. Each panel, measuring 3 ft. 4 in. × 1 ft. 8 in. × 1½ in. thick, can be removed. All edges are chamfered showing neat V-joints. The panels are primarily intended for use with Hill's Presweld beams on a 40-in. module (Fig. 152, p. 177).—Ed.

members being unnecessary except for bracing if frames are used, or where joints in the sheeting occur.

Nailing of adjoining sheets should be in pairs, not staggered, and should not exceed 4–5 in. apart.

Before considering the main groups under which the majority of different types are most conveniently classified, mention should be made of one, which, on account of its larger scale and more structural character cannot be judged in the same category as any other material.

Woodwool Slabs

Of much the same composition as chip-board, with the exception that wood shavings – instead of finer material – are impregnated with resins and compressed into large slabs, often 6 ft. × 2 ft. × 2 in. thick – woodwool is frequently used to provide a large-scale, rough-texture finish in buildings of exceptional size, such as large exhibition halls.

When a paint-sprayed colour-finish is applied, the effect can be extremely impressive especially when very large areas are treated in this way.

It can be regarded almost as a structural material – it is common practice to erect it as shuttering for concrete. The concrete can be poured direct onto the woodwool slabs, bonding with them to form a composite floor and ceiling.

THE CHIEF TYPES OF CEILING- AND WALL-BOARDS, WITH COMPARATIVE PRICES, SCHEDULED IN SIX GROUPS:

GROUP I   VENEERED BOARDS

Type	Special Features or Uses	Approx. Cost per sq. ft.		Sizes
Veneered Hardboards Figured Oak Sapele Figured Australian Walnut Figured Avodire Sycamore Bird's-Eye Maple	High-class wood panelling for offices, shops, showrooms Restaurants and hotels Also furniture and fitments	$\frac{5}{32}$ in. thick 1s. 9d. 1s. 9d. 2s. 10d. 2s. 6d. 2s. 3d. 3s. 4d.		5 ft., 6 ft. and 7 × 4 ft. and Flush Door Sizes
Veneered Chip-boards Figured Oak Sapele Australian Walnut Sycamore	Chip-boards up to ¾ in. are veneered to provide solid panelling where structural strength is important	½ in. thick 2s. 6d. 2s. 6d. 3s. 9d. 3s.	¾ in. thick 3s. 3s. 4s. 3d. 3s. 6d	8 × 4 ft.

Note: Grain of wood veneers will run parallel with long edges.

GROUP 2   PLASTER BOARDS

Type	Thickness	Special Features or Uses	Cost	Finishes
Plaster, Wall & Ceiling Board	$\frac{1}{4}$–$\frac{1}{2}$ in.	Solid plaster core with stout paper both sides, ready for painting	5d.–6d.	Paint or distemper

GROUP 3   DECORATIVE LAMINATED PLASTICS

Type	Colours	Thickness & Cost		Finishes
		$\frac{3}{16}$ in. single-sided	$\frac{5}{32}$ in. double-sided	
Formica Patterns				
Linette	Pink, red, brown, grey, green, buff, blue	4s. 3d.	8s. 3d.	Matt or glossy
Onyx	Blue, grey, green, buff, red			
Woodgrains	Bleached mahogany, bird's-eye maple, cherry mahogany, red mahogany, bleached grey, primavera, dark mahogany	4s. 3d.	11s.	ditto
Realwood	Sapele mahogany	8s.	16s.	ditto
Softglow	Ivory, steel blue, dove grey, two greens, scarlet red	4s. 10d.	10s. 3d.	ditto
For Cigarette-proof finish add 9d. per sq. ft.				

		.050 in.	$\frac{1}{8}$ in.	
Warerite				
Melamine Patterns	Weave – buff, grey	4s.	6s. 3d.	Standard Satin finish
	Finaweave – buff, yellow, green, pink, blue and grey	4s.	6s. 3d.	ditto
	Marble, mottle, maple, oak, walnut	4s.	6s. 3d.	ditto
Melamine Colour Textures	2 blues, grey, brown and 2 greens	4s.	6s. 3d.	ditto
Urea, Plain Colours	White, ivory	4s. 3d.	6s. 6d.	ditto
Phenolic Patterns and Colours	Mahogany, oak, walnut, black (solid throughout)	3s. 6d.	5s. 9d.	ditto

For glossy finish add 3d. per sq. ft. for .050 in. thickness and 6d. for $\frac{1}{8}$ in.
For cigarette-proof finish add 3d. per sq. ft. for .050 in. thickness and 6d. for $\frac{1}{8}$ in.

Tables continued on page 185

152

FLOOR. 152. *Studded rubber tiles on the floor of the entrance hall and dining room of the experimental secondary modern school at Wokingham designed by the Architects' Branch of the Ministry of Education. It is claimed that this flooring saves rubber, is easy to clean and stays cleaner than any other form of rubber floor (Brynmawr Rubber Company). The ceiling here is composed of lightweight vermiculite concrete panels (see footnote, p. 173).*

153
153

153

154

155
155

FLOORS. 153. *Linoleum tiles.* 153a. *Sheet linoleum with a plaid pattern.* 153b. *Linoleum with a square, marbled pattern.* 154. *Sheet rubber flooring inlaid to a special large-scale design.* 155. *Non-vitreous tiles in a light buff colour in the entrance hall of a school.* 155a. *Glazed hexagonal tiles in a bath-room.*

FLOORS. 156. *The random-laid flooring at the Waterloo Air Terminal Buffet, London, consists of pieces of broken white marble and broken slabs of coloured pre-cast concrete, in blues and greys, set in cement.*
157. *Cork tiles of varying colours on a board room floor.* 157a. *Cork tiles in a domestic interior.*

156

157a

157

158

159

CEILING AND WALL. 158. *A Conference Room ceiling of absorbent fibrous plaster panels, 5 ft. 4 in. wide, precast in sections in the form of a grille and backed by a one-inch-thick glass-fibre blanket, to increase sound-absorbtion, at Pilkington Brothers' premises, St. James's, London. The all-glass table is electrically warmed. The clock-wall facing is polished plate glass, silvered, with a medium stippled surface (Architect: Kenneth Cheesman). 159. Fixing the glass-fibre blanket at the back of the plaster. (See also Fig. 170, p. 189.)*

CEILINGS. 160. *An egg-crate timber ceiling in a Manchester showroom is suspended by chains and painted white, hides the ugly, original ceiling of converted premises and allows the frames for draping cloth to be hung in any position (Architects: A. S. Buckley and A. H. Knowles).* 161. *A ceiling decorated with a rosette-patterned wallpaper in another Manchester showroom for the Cotton Board Colour Design and Style Centre (Architects: Robert and Roger Nicholson).* 162. *The suspended ceiling and projecting boxes of fibrous plaster at the Royal Festival Hall, London (Architects: Robert H. Matthew and J. L. Martin, L.C.C.). The plaster is formed to contain light fittings and the sides of the boxes are faced with dark blue flock paper.*

160

162

163

164

WALLS. 163. *The glazed wall partly boarded and covered with brightly coloured wallpaper which separates the junior assembly hall from the junior entrance hall at a primary school, Coventry (Architects: Richard Sheppard and Partners).* 164. *Corrugated plywood panelling with a basis of Cellobond synthetic resin adhesive (British Resin Products).* 165. *Telephone booths at the Royal Festival Hall, London, are faced in front with veneered plywood and lined inside at the top and sides with perforated aluminium. The rear wall is faced with cork tiling.* 166. *(facing page). The Royal Festival Hall upper restaurant, London, has a glazed wall separating it from one of the main staircases. The wall surface at the top right is of polished Derbyshire marble.*

165

167

WALLS. 167. *The waiting area in the main reception room of the Qantas Empire Airways Office, Piccadilly, London (Architects: James Cubitt and Partners) has a wall of Belge Bleu marble with a strip of mirror above it which appears to prolong the hanging of sycamore slats and so increases the sense of space. Above the slats are cold cathode fluorescent tubes. The screen on the right is of plain and reeded glass.* 168. *A ladies' shoe shop in Bond Street, London (Architect: Ellis Somake) has one entire wall of the reception area faced with verd-antique marble slabs.* 169. *Another interior view of the same shop shows an interesting combination of materials and finishes. The left-hand wall consists of polished mahogany-veneered plywood panels; the right-hand wall is a rough-textured plaster, painted white. The metal plant-trellis and fitted carpet were specially designed.*

168   169

Type	Thick-ness	Special Features or Uses	Approx. Cost per sq. ft.	Finishes Applicable
FIBRE LAMINATED BOARDS Essex Board	$\frac{3}{16}$ in.	Somewhat soft, but light and inexpensive wall and ceiling board	4d.	Paint or dis-temper
FIBRE INSULATION BOARDS Celotex, TenTest and many others	$\frac{5}{16}$–$\frac{1}{2}$ in.	For thermal and sound insulation of walls, par-titions and ceilings	4d.–6d.	Paint or dis-temper
FIBRE MEDIUM HARDBOARD Sundeala and others	$\frac{1}{4}$–$\frac{1}{2}$ in.	Medium hard surface for oil paint	5d.– 1s. 6d.	Paint or dis-temper
FIBRE HARDBOARDS Celotex, Sundeala, Masonite, etc.	$\frac{1}{8}$– $\frac{3}{16}$ in.	Hard, smooth surface for paint finishes for walls, partitions, ceilings, fix-tures and furniture	6d.–1s.	Paint, distemper and wallpaper
RESIN-BONDED CHIP-BOARDS Weyroc, Plimberite, etc.	$\frac{1}{2}$ in. & $\frac{3}{4}$ in.	Of solid structure, suit-able for single-board par-titions, and as core for wood veneers	1s. 1$\frac{1}{2}$d. –1s. 6d.	Paint, distemper, or can be left natural and pol-ished
SPECIALITIES Flameproofed Hardboard	$\frac{1}{8}$ in.	Suitable for exhibition stand construction	10d.	Paint, Distemper or wall paper
Embossed Hardboard (various profiles, fluted, reeded, etc.)	$\frac{1}{8}$ in.	Low relief, fluted and reeded surface, suitable for shop interiors, exhi-bition stands and display work	10d. –1s.	Paint or dis-temper
Perforated Hardboard	$\frac{1}{8}$ in.	Suitable for exhibition stands and display work	1s.	Paint or dis-temper
Leather Board	$\frac{1}{8}$ in.	Imitation Spanish grain-leather finish available in dark brown and light-natural hide, also green and morocco red	1s. 6d.	

4. FIBROUS PLASTER

Fibrous plaster is unquestionably one of the most versatile of all interior finishes, and one which is liable to be underrated or spurned because of its association with the reproduction of endless miles of traditional ornament in

o

Type	Thick-ness	Special Features or Uses	Approx. Cost per sq. ft.	Finishes
Flat Sheet (Poilite)	$\frac{3}{16}$–$\frac{1}{2}$ in.	Suitable for lining sheds, garages, etc.	4d.– 1s. 6d.	Paints, distempers, after special primer
Flexible Flat Sheet	$\frac{1}{8}$ in.	Curved lining work	5d.	ditto
3-in. Corrugated Sheet	$\frac{1}{4}$ in.	Ceilings or vertical wall lining	7d.	ditto
6-in. Corrugated	$\frac{1}{4}$ in.	Larger-scale ceilings or walls	8d.	ditto
Trafford Tile	$\frac{1}{4}$ in.	Ceiling or wall lining	8d.	ditto
1½-in. Fluted Sheet	$\frac{3}{8}$ in.	Wall lining, particularly suitable for fireplaces	1s. 1½d.	ditto
Asbestos Wall Boards	2 mm. –$\frac{1}{4}$ in.	Fireproof wall lining suitable for exhibitions, theatres, cinemas	1s. 3d. –3s. 1d.	ditto
Asbestos Mill-board	$\frac{1}{8}$–$\frac{1}{4}$ in.	Suitable for fireproof linings, fitting behind radiators, etc.	1s.–2s.	ditto

GROUP 6   LAMINATED PLASTIC BOARDS

Type	Thick-ness	Special Features or Uses	Approx. Cost per sq. ft.	Finishes
Laminated Plastic Boards	$\frac{1}{16}$– 2¼ in.	Smooth, hard surfaces both sides	1s. 6d. –7s.	Supplied in standard brown and black satin finish or 'Decorated'
Holoplast (Structural Panels)	1 in.	Flush doors and other panels in which flatness is essential	8s. 10d.	(See note at end of Group 3)

low relief, or superficially applied decoration.

Although it lends itself admirably to imitating the appearance of other materials, textures, etc. when required, the whole technique should not be condemned because it is often misapplied.

It is just as capable of playing an essential part in contemporary design and construction as it has ever been in the past, providing the principle of the technique is understood, and its limitations borne in mind.

Consisting as the manufacturing process does of casting from a mould, the greatest benefit is obtained when a large number of exactly similar units are required, as the initial cost of a mould may be heavy. Very large domes for instance can be constructed by repetition of a single segment at relatively low cost compared with any other material or form of construction. The actual skin is seldom more than $\frac{3}{4}$ in. to 1 in., and the stiffness is produced by ribs of suitable depth and shape at the back. These ribs consist in most cases of surprisingly flimsy soft wood, and the separate members of the skeleton are connected to one another by nothing more than strips of cotton scrim dipped in plaster and bound or tied at intersections – the whole becoming one homogeneous mass, and setting to form an extremely tough and rigid structure.

There are practically no limits to the forms that can be produced in this medium. Very large units can be constructed (from 24 to 30 feet super being quite usual) and erection on the site is a comparatively simple operation – connection to wood or metal hangers being frequently on the same principle as in the sections themselves, by wadding with scrim cloth dipped in almost liquid plaster.

An interesting example of the functional part fibrous plaster construction can play in the technical problems of to-day can be seen in a false ceiling in a Conference Room, which on account of its unusual curved surface, would have presented acoustic difficulties if faced in the normal way in hard plaster.

Fibreglass blanket was recommended by technical experts as the most suitable material, but this, while providing efficiency, is not rigid enough to be self-supporting, and is too rough and unsightly to pass as a finish in a dignified interior of this kind if applied on the face of a rigid ceiling in another material.

Normal fibrous plaster construction provided the solution, which was to construct a simple all-over cellular ceiling, the fibreglass being accommodated in strips between the constructional ribs at the back (see detail drawing – Fig. 170). The spacing and size of holes was worked out to give an over-all ratio of $\frac{1}{1\frac{1}{2}}$ void to solid, which was the minimum figure recommended to provide adequate sound absorbtion.

In contemporary architectural design it is most appropriately used for the construction of entire ceilings of such interiors as theatres, concert halls, cinemas, etc. no matter how elaborately contoured or perforated they may have to be to conform with the demands of modern acoustics, lighting and ventilation.

A more conclusive example of this could hardly be found than the ceiling structure of the Royal Festival Hall (Fig. 162, p. 181). Fibrous plaster was also used for the cast shell of the boxes seen in the same illustration.

5. GLASS*

Glass is a material which does not seem to play as large a part in contemporary design as its characteristic properties – imperviousness to moisture, durability, hard surface and varying degrees of translucency – might lead us to expect.

Occasionally we notice outstanding examples of its sound and imaginative application, the majority of instances being in shop design, but even here it is seldom that anything more unusual is seen than clear polished plate, with a few instances of fluted and reeded glasses.

When we consider the many different kinds of glass manufactured, each with quite a large selection of patterns, textures, and in some cases, colours, it is remarkable that so few contemporary designers ever seem to use more than two or three.

Is it that they are prejudiced against the material because of its inherent coldness? Do they so much dislike all the available patterns and textures, or is it that the architecture schools and technical schools are outstandingly weak in teaching applications of this particular material?

Whatever the reason, it can hardly be said that glass is unduly expensive, for some of the rolled glasses can be had for as little as 10*d.* per square foot.

Rolled Glass

Many of these have a simple ribbed surface on one side which is entirely in keeping with the contemporary idiom and for this reason alone they deserve to be better known and more generally used.

They can be supplied in a maximum width of 40 in. and up to 10 ft. in length (the ribs running parallel with the length). A few of these glasses are sufficiently substantial (approximately $\frac{1}{4}$ in. thick) to play a semi-structural part in screens, partitions, etc. where – providing reasonable protection is given – their edges may safely be exposed.

Thick Roughcast Plate Glass

Thicknesses of $\frac{1}{2}$ in., $\frac{3}{4}$ in. and 1 in. have extremely pleasant textures, and although the thicker substances are somewhat costly, the $\frac{1}{2}$ in. roughcast can be obtained at around 4*s.* 6*d.* per square foot.

Toughened Glass

This, being approximately four to five times as strong as ordinary plate glass, is capable of playing a fully structural role in interior work, and is largely used for protective screening in machine shops.

It is also useful for increasing the safe load on glass shelving or in cases where the span between supports is more than ordinary plate glass could stand up to.

* See also *New Ways of Building.*—Ed.

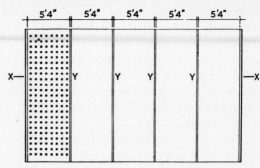

PLAN OF CEILING

170. *Plan, section and details of an acoustic plaster ceiling in a London conference room. (See also Figs. 158 and 159 on p. 180).*

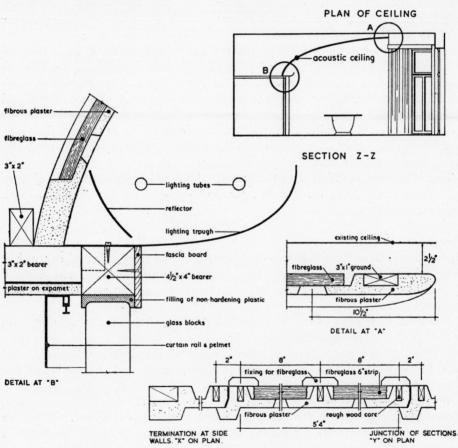

SECTION Z–Z

acoustic ceiling

fibrous plaster

fibreglass

3" x 2"

lighting tubes

reflector

lighting trough

fascia board

3" x 2" bearer

4½" x 4" bearer

plaster on expamet

filling of non-hardening plastic

glass blocks

curtain rail & pelmet

DETAIL AT "B"

existing ceiling

fibreglass   3" x 1" ground

2½"

fibrous plaster

10½"

DETAIL AT "A"

2"   8"   8"   2"

fixing for fibreglass   fibreglass 6" strip

fibrous plaster   rough wood core

5'4"

TERMINATION AT SIDE WALLS "X" ON PLAN.

JUNCTION OF SECTIONS "Y" ON PLAN

189

It is well known that the process of toughening glass greatly increases its resistance to impact, bending, twisting and temperature extremes, with the result that it can safely withstand severe blows on its surfaces. It is not so generally known that the edges of the glass are vulnerable in a way which differs from ordinary glass, and that a blow on the edge with a hammer or other hard object, will sometimes cause the whole plate to disintegrate into small dice-like pieces.

It is essential therefore to protect the edges of a toughened plate as much as possible, but this does not mean that all edges have to be framed. Protection can often be effected less obviously by incorporating in the design some shock member which prevents contact in much the same way as a motor-car bumper protects an easily damaged wing.

Another important point governing the use of toughened glass is that all shaping, drilling, or any other form of work required, must be done before the plate is toughened, because, for the reason given above, any attempt to work the edges or drill after the plate has been toughened, may result in the whole plate shattering.

As the process is a highly technical one involving the re-heating of the glass, toughening can only be undertaken at the works, and this glass will naturally take longer to supply than unprocessed glass.

The only glass to which the process can be applied is polished plate glass in thicknesses from $\frac{3}{16}$–$1\frac{1}{2}$ in. and in sizes up to 36×84 in. This includes black polished plate glass.

Coloured Opal Glass

Opal Glass such as 'Vitrolite' provides an exceedingly hygienic and decorative finish for the wall lining of kitchens, bathrooms and lavatories, and it has a natural fire finish which is hard, easily cleaned and impervious to grease, stains and acids.

It is obtainable in standard ashlar sizes 8×12 in., 10×15 in., 12×18 in., and 15×15 in. – the standard thickness being $\frac{5}{16}$ in.

Colours available are green, primrose, eggshell, turquoise, shell pink, pearl grey, black, white and cream. It is also produced in an agate form – which has a marbled effect – in green.

The average cost of the material in ashlar sizes is 31*s*. to 35*s*. per square yard, according to colour, and the fixing costs are in the region of 40*s*. per square yard. Fixing is normally by means of a special non-hardening mastic to a cement-screeded surface, the back of the 'Vitrolite' being ribbed to form a better key for the mastic.

'Vitrolite' can also be effectively used as a finish to window sills, kitchen tables or work tops, shelves, bar and counter tops, and to a limited extent in furniture (sliding doors for sideboards, cupboards, etc. and table tops).

Glass with Metal Components

Where metal components are used in conjunction with non-toughened glass, great care must be taken to insulate the glass from direct contact with the metal.

In the use of channels or frames, this is generally done by means of wash-leather between the glass and metal, but where screws are used for fixing glass, mirrors, etc. a rigid distance sleeve should be provided slightly longer than the thickness of the glass (metal tube will serve the purpose) so that when the screw is tightened it cannot bear on the surface of the glass.

It is a very common sight to see glass which has fractured from a hole because the screw has been over-tightened.

Ordinary non-toughened glass will, however, safely stand quite a considerable clamping pressure, providing this is applied evenly over a wide area. For such a purpose a very much over-size hole should be drilled through the glass and a flat metal disc or plate used to distribute the pressure.

Even here it is always advisable to use an insulating 'washer' of some resilient material such as sheet rubber, or P.V.C. plastic. The latter material is especially useful in connection with glass and metal, as the polished sheet adheres to polished surfaces, preventing glass shelves, for instance, from sliding out of place when supported on metal brackets.

The P.V.C. sheet material can now be obtained in a form which is as transparent as glass, so that it is practically invisible.

Glass Blocks

These can be just as effectively applied in interior as in exterior design to form self-supporting translucent screens or partitions. In addition to their light-giving properties and decorative finish on both sides, they also provide a high degree of sound insulation and are extensively used in office blocks and similar buildings, in the upper walls of corridors which serve rooms on either side. Ample light is obtained in the corridor from the office windows on each side.

An average cost of glass-block walling supplied and fixed is 15s. per square foot for the large (8×8 in.) block and 20s. for the small (6×6 in.)

Embossed Glass

This is an expression used in the glass industry to denote the product of any type of decorative process whether brilliant cutting, acid etching, or sand blasting.

Acid Embossing

Various grades of stippled surface – coarse, medium or fine – can be produced on clear glass giving it a semi-transparent effect and an evenly stippled surface texture.

A variety of grades of obscuration can be produced by means of acid, depending on the duration of the acid attack; and by masking portions of the glass with a preparation which is capable of resisting the acid, designs of any degree of intricacy can be carried out.

Sandblasting
Designs and decorative effects can also be carried out by 'sandblasting' which, as its name implies, consists of masking the parts which are not to be treated and exposing the rest to the abrasive action of sandblast.

The longer the action continues, the deeper the sand eats into the surface of the glass, until, if continued, it would cut right through to the other side.

Brilliant Cutting
This process consists of engraving the glass by holding and guiding it over a grinding wheel which is revolving in a vertical plane. A V-shaped cut is produced which can either be left with a whitish matt finish direct from the stone wheel, or finished with a wood and felt wheel until it is quite clear and 'brilliant'.

These processes are much used in the fabrication of signs and lettered panels – the acid or sandblast letters being frequently filled in with paint, gold or metal leaf.

Flex-a-Glass
This material, formerly marketed under different names, consists of thin silvered sheet glass mounted on a fabric back and cut in both directions to form small units $2 \times \frac{1}{2}$ in., 2×1 in., or 1×1 in. The units when cut hold together on the fabric which can then be applied to flat or curved surfaces by means of a special mastic (Bostik C.).

It is sometimes used as a decorative finish on unsightly columns in shops and shopwindows. It is mainly used for window beds, and for covering display stands and bases.

Plyglass
Plyglass is a three-ply glass laminate of which the two outside plies are of thin sheet glass, with a diffusing membrane of glass fibres sandwiched between the two. The glass fibre interlayer diffuses light, cuts out glare, and reduces heat losses in cold weather by one-third, as compared with normal single sheet or plate glazing. It is not a new material, being in almost every respect similar to a glass product which was comparatively well-known before the war under the name of Thermalux (see *New Ways of Building*). It is recommended for roof glazing, laylights, clerestory glazing and over-transom lighting of shops, classrooms and many other structural purposes, while numerous equally suitable applications can be found in connection with interior work.

Obscured glass such as sandblast plate glass, while providing efficient diffusion collects dirt very quickly in its rough texture, and it is here that plyglass offers a great advantage with its polished surfaces both sides. The particular form of obscuration provided by the glass fibre interlayer is rather more efficient than most of the figured rolled glasses, for use where a high degree of privacy is desirable (bathrooms, etc.)

It can be strongly recommended for fanlights over doors, translucent screens and internal partitions, for diffusing artificial light, and in connection with display, provision of translucent backgrounds behind lettering, and many more specialized purposes.

An important point to note is that plyglass cannot be cut after manufacture, consequently exact glazing sizes must be specified on orders. It is equally important to indicate which dimension is to be the 'height' when glazed, because this determines in which direction the glass fibres have to run.

Glazing is in all other respects identical with the glazing of normal glass.

Plyglass is available in thicknesses and sizes as follows.

Thickness	Vertical Panels	Horizontal Panels	White	Coloured
$\frac{7}{32}$ in.	up to 40×30 in.	up to 40×15 in.		
$\frac{1}{4}$ in.	up to 60×42 in.	up to 60×25 in.	4s. per sq. ft.	5s. per sq. ft.
$\frac{3}{8}$ in.	over 60×42 in.	over 60×25 in.	6s. 6d. per sq. ft.	7s. 6d. per sq. ft.

6. TRANSLUCENT PLASTICS

Corrugated Sheeting

This material, which can justly claim to be a new material in that it has only recently emerged from the development stage, is a very tough laminated sheet built up of two translucent sheets with a diffusing interlayer of glass fibre between.

It is produced in corrugated form to the same gauge as standard galvanized iron and corrugated asbestos sheeting, to increase the strength and rigidity of the sheet, and to enable it to be used in conjunction with these materials for roofing and wall cladding. The sheets nest into these existing corrugated materials and are fixed in exactly the same way, causing no interruption in the structural system.

It is available in sheets 8 ft. long by 30 in. wide, both in the normal gauge and the 'big six' gauge, and there is also a special form moulded to fit the Trafford type of asbestos sheeting.

The material is considerably lighter than glass, is weather-resistant, and shatterproof. It diffuses light, cutting out glare, and provides a certain degree of heat insulation by excluding 65 per cent of the infra-red heat rays of the sun.

It can be nailed, bolted, screwed or sawn with ordinary tools without splitting or splintering.

Although primarily produced as a translucent structural material, there is no doubt that many uses will be found for this in interior work, the most obvious being for luminous false ceilings, translucent screens and partitions; but it will also serve many other purposes.

The standard material is a greyish-white, but it is also produced in a limited range of colour – pale green, pale pink and light yellow.

Translucent Wall Blocks

An interlocking hollow translucent wall block, suitable for internal partitions where light transmission, lightness and ease of erection are required, is now moulded from clear polystyrene or cellulose acetate. The size of the standard unit is $7\frac{13}{16} \times 7\frac{13}{16}$ in. on face, and $1\frac{11}{16}$ in. deep, and its weight is slightly under 1 lb.

Interlocking fins ensure alignment of the blocks, and provide rigidity to the panel without the necessity of adhesives, but if a panel needs to be waterproof, a suitable mastic used for jointing will ensure a watertight finish.

The outward appearance of the block is very similar to that of the Insulight Glass block (see *New Ways of Building*) and the construction of walls and panels is much the same with the exception that no jointing material is required here.

Like the glass block, it cannot be expected to carry more than its own weight, and panels should be restricted to sixteen courses in height, unless additional supporting structure is introduced.

Blocks can be shaped and cut with a saw if required.

They are not fire-resisting, combustibility being about the same as that of untreated wood of the same thickness. Blocks should not therefore be used where temperatures exceed 140°F.

Certain cleaning fluids – turpentine and abrasives – are harmful, mild soap and water being recommended instead for cleaning, followed by a soft dry cloth.

7. MARBLE AND GRANITE AS WALL LINING

As already stated in the sub-section dealing with floor finishes – the cost of marble in this country is unfortunately prohibitive, yet there is hardly an alternative material which is equally suitable to the entrances and staircase halls of public buildings, unless it is granite, which is even more costly.

Surprising as it may seem, this final cost is not due to high duties on imported material, for the cost of home-quarried raw material is a mere shilling or two less than similar types from Italy or Jugoslavia. In view of the fact that Continental marbles offer so much greater selection, and are more even in texture, they must be regarded as better value if they are to be judged fairly.

The high cost is entirely due to labour and cost of sawing the raw material into $\frac{3}{4}$-in. thick slabs, the minimum thickness which is considered practicable. Only exceptionally hard material such as quartzite is cut as thin as $\frac{3}{8}$ in. or $\frac{1}{2}$ in.

Fixing is usually by means of 'cramps' or metal anchors, grouted into holes drilled at the back of the marble and cement-fixed into the wall – in much the same way as rag bolts. A very fine Parian cement is used for the purpose.

Marble is also fixed by means of screws to wood or other frames in shop-fitting work, but care must be taken to ensure that no bending stress is put upon the material, otherwise it may fracture in the same way that glass will break under similar pressure.

It must not be supposed that marble retains its polish indefinitely for, if it is not cleaned periodically and given a protective coat of wax polish, it will lose its lustre and eventually deteriorate.

Granite, on the other hand, will almost indefinitely retain a polished surface and this elimination of maintenance cost to a large extent off-sets its considerably higher initial cost.

A material of similar nature to marble but much less frequently used is Hoptonwood stone, which is quarried in the district around Matlock, Derbyshire. Its colour-range varies between grey and brown, and its figure and texture are in some respects similar to granite.

Another British marble, Grey Derbyshire Fossil previously little known, has been used on a comparatively large scale in the Royal Festival Hall for the wall lining of crush halls, staircases and corridors.

8. TILES AS WALL FINISH

Ceramic (clay) tiles have been used from the earliest times as a wall and floor finish. Properly fixed on correctly prepared walls, tiling will outlast most building materials.

All types of fired clay tiles provide durable, permanent surfaces which are easily cleaned – hence the popularity of the finish for canteens, kitchens, hospitals, bathrooms and food shops.

A large selection of accessories is available in the form of coved angles, skirtings, cappings, and a variety of recessed wall fittings for lavatories and bathrooms.

Plain floor tiles are available principally in earth colours, grey, buff, red, chocolate and black.

Vitreous Tiles

These are much harder than ordinary tiles, but are not normally available in sizes larger than 3×3 in. A large range of more subtle colours is produced including mottled and textured surfaces. Standard sizes are: $6 \times 6 \times \frac{1}{2}$ in.; $4 \times 4 \times \frac{1}{2}$ in.; $3 \times 3 \times \frac{1}{2}$ in.; $6 \times 3 \times \frac{1}{2}$ in.; $6 \times 2 \times \frac{1}{2}$ in.; $6 \times 1 \times \frac{1}{2}$ in.

Ceramic Mosaic

This is made of the same material in plain or vitreous body in small units approximately $1 \times 1 \times \frac{3}{16}$ in. thick. These are often supplied ready mounted on paper, and fixing consists of inverting the paper, bedding the mosaic squares in the cement screed and, when the cement has set sufficiently, wetting and cleaning off the paper from the face.

The use of this material is unfortunately so rare in this country that it is difficult to find any fixers sufficiently skilled to do the work.

It is nevertheless a most effective and beautiful medium for wall, floor, or ceiling surfaces, and it is extensively used in Italy for bathrooms, and a great variety of purposes in which its small scale and very slight colour variation combine to produce a very pleasing texture.

The cost of the material is from 160s. per sq. yard but the fixing, owing to the skill it requires, might add as much as a further 80s. per sq. yard.

9. CEMENT FINISHES

Cement renderings consisting of white or coloured cement mixed with specially graded sand, can be applied direct to concrete to provide a decorative finish to concrete block cavity walls or in-situ walls where the joints or marks of shuttering are outlined on the finished surface.

A great variety of surface textures can be produced during the application of the rendering coat, but this fact sometimes proves more of a disadvantage than an advantage since the craftsman is liable to get carried away by his own ingenuity, producing ever more irritating and fussy surface patterns which detract from, rather than add to, the general effect.

We do occasionally see wall surfaces with irresistibly attractive textures, and these are invariably the result of some quite simple technique – the natural laying on of the plastic material with a particular size and shape of wood float in a particular manner – and would probably turn out to be a perfectly natural and comfortable operation.

This supposition is borne out by the fact that we find attractive textures much more frequently on old and quite primitive buildings, both in this country and on the Continent, than we do in modern work.

It is practically impossible, therefore, to specify a textured finish of this subtle type to-day with any likelihood of achieving it, unless the architect or designer can either submit an actual sample to the contractor, or else is prepared to meet the craftsman on the site and evolve a satisfactory solution by trial and error.

Tyrolean Finish

It is largely as a result of this situation that the texture known as Tyrolean finish has become so much in favour. This type of facing owes its popularity to its decorative and uniform appearance and to the fact that it can be applied quickly and easily by means of a simply operated machine.

The finish, although it appears fairly dense, is actually built up of adhering particles to a total thickness of $\frac{1}{4}$–$\frac{5}{16}$ in., and consequently crazing is extremely unlikely. The mixture, which is flicked onto the surface from a revolving brush, consists of white or coloured cement and specially graded sand.

Owing, however, to the difficulty of manipulating the machine in a very low position, a plain 12–18-in. plinth is the finish usually adopted at ground level.

Tyrolean finish can be equally attractively applied to ceilings, the underside of galleries in theatres or cinemas, and similar surfaces, and if the full texture is too rough, it can be lightly rubbed with a carborundum or other suitable stone to flatten the high points yet leave the valleys and indentations untouched.

10. PAINTS AND ALLIED FINISHES

During the war and post-war years, many innovations and new types of material have been introduced on the market with varying degrees of success.

Many of these take the form of special-purpose finishes, anti-rust, anti-condensation, damp-proof – to mention a few – while others are the result of research laboratory experiments with the object of improving the quality or durability of the finish, avoiding the use of base materials in short supply, or making indirect gains such as reduced cost through speeding application or eliminating preparation work, thereby effecting a saving in labour costs.

By far the most conspicuous feature in the paint field during the past few years has been the growing popularity of emulsion paints of one kind or another, and this is entirely owing to their cost-saving claims by eliminating the necessity for a sealer and special undercoating.

At a time when labour costs are approaching six times that of the materials used, any reduction in the time of application saves money, and it is understandable that such claims prove a powerful selling factor.

As there are a large number of quite different types of paint available, a brief glossary of the most important, mentioning any special advantages or peculiarities, should be of assistance in selecting the type best suited to the particular work in hand, and it may be of additional interest and use to arrange them as nearly as possible in order of quality (see p. 198).

As a general rule it can be taken that the finest quality finish will be the most expensive, consequently the same order will also provide a rough guide to the comparative cost.

Preparation for Paint Work

All wood must be well rubbed down and be perfectly clean and free from grease, loose dust, and so on, before any paint is applied. For normal oil paint, whether flat or gloss, an efficient alkali-resisting sealer is essential, followed by at least one undercoat, which should be of lead base for a gloss finish, or lithopone base for eggshell and flat finishes.

Sealers and Primers

A number of good general-purpose sealers are available, and most of the reputable paint manufacturers recommend one to suit the precise paint and finish

GLOSSARY OF PRINCIPAL PAINT TYPES
(arranged in ascending order of quality)

SIZE-BOUND DISTEMPER	Suitable as a temporary finish for new plaster during drying out period.
NON-OIL-BOUND DISTEMPER (Casein base)	Improvement on above. Will not brush off when touched.
OIL-BOUND DISTEMPER	Top grade 'waterpaint' (Ceilingite in this category).
EMULSION PAINTS (Synthetic resin base emulsified in water)	Based on white powder, so produce chalky colours, best regarded as tinted whites.
FLAT OIL	For strong, intense colours, also better durability.
EGGSHELL OIL	Semi-gloss finishes of various grades.
WHITE LEAD GLOSS PAINT	Genuine lead paint based on white lead. For greatest durability.
FULL GLOSS OIL	Normally based on zinc oxide and titanium for better flowing properties.
ENAMELS	An obsolete name for specially prepared products before paint had reached its present-day degree of high gloss.
LACQUERS (shellac)	Based on china wood oil. Also 2–4 hour lacquers, transparent or opaque. Better covering power in one coat than gloss paints.
GLAZES	Heat-treated oil with extender pigment to act as base for stainers (colour ground in oil).
VARNISH (Oleo-resin)	Frequently referred to as 'copal' varnish for various special purposes.
VARNISH (Synthetic)	Phenolic type. Alkyd type – noted for retention of gloss.
CELLULOSE	Nitro-cellulose base with pigment and resins. Does not rely on oxidization but on evaporation of solvents. There is consequently no good *brushing* cellulose paint. *Must* be sprayed on as brushing in second coat pulls up first.

required. These are, in the main, in pigmented form, and have been developed for the treatment of *new* Portland cement, asbestos, and similar sheeting, as well as composition boards.

Two coats of pigmented sealer should be applied to new Portland cement when it has dried out from the backing, after which, for the most durable finish, two coats of undercoating should follow before the finishing coat. This also applies to brick or stone surfaces, in such places as cellars, cold storage buildings, swimming baths, etc.

One coat of sealer should be sufficient for asbestos sheeting and composition boards, providing that the sheeting is dry, and is treated on the front, back and all edges, so that moisture cannot be taken up from the atmosphere.

Many of these sealers are also supplied in transparent form for waterproofing, and are recommended for the exterior wall surfaces whether cement, stone, brick or stucco. Two coats are applied during dry weather, both being well brushed into the surface. The interior surface should then be stripped and left bare for the moisture in the wall to be drawn through, after which it will be safe to complete internal decoration.

Pigmented primers with special properties are also available for such purposes as re-decorating over loose and perished distempered or painted surfaces. These effectively seal porous surfaces, giving a firm foundation for subsequent coats of paint or distemper. Being pigmented white, their primers can easily be tinted with stainer and can consequently be used in place of one undercoat. An additional advantage of using a good primer is that the sounder base produced enables finishing coats to be applied with the maximum speed and coverage, both of which save money. The surface must, of course, be rubbed down and thoroughly cleaned before primer is applied. All primers must be allowed to dry hard before applying undercoats or finish.

Plastic paints may also very usefully be employed as a filler for cracks or holes in plaster, wood, etc., and on rough surfaces of all kinds surface irregularities can be completely hidden. It can also be sandpapered after 48 hours if necessary.

Anti-Rust Paints
For the painting of iron and steel work which is liable to rust, special primer undercoating is now available, in a reasonable range of pale colours. This paint has remarkable adhesive properties, and offers great resistance to moisture, sea air, and salt spray. One coat is sufficient as a priming for interior finishes, but two coats are necessary for external work or severe conditions of wear and tear.

Typical Specification for Interior Paint Work
New work: ceilings and walls. All lime-free (neutral) plasters should be primed when dry with a reliable primer.

For eggshell or gloss oil finish. Two coats of undercoating for the appropriate finish. Rub down between coats. One coat eggshell or gloss finish.

For flat or matt finish. Apply two coats of flat drying oil paint coat over coat.

For water paint. Apply one coat of primer followed by two coats of washable water paint.

Old work (previously painted). Remove loose or flaking paint or distemper and thoroughly clean surface. Use stopper and/or filler where necessary. Patch-prime bare parts and all parts made good, with primer.

Eggshell and gloss oil finish. Apply one or two coats of undercoating for appropriate finish. Follow with one coat eggshell or gloss finish.

Matt oil finish. Apply two coats flat-drying oil paint coat over coat.

Water paint finish. Thoroughly clean surface. Patch-prime all bare parts with wall primer. Make good with mixture of plaster of paris and water paint paste, rub down smooth and prime all parts made good with primer. Follow with two coats of washable water paint.

Special Purpose Paints
Aluminium Paint, besides being used as a bright metallic paint finish, is exten-

sively used as a sealer for priming metal work before applying other finishes on account of its rust-preventive properties. It is also used as a sealer on woods such as teak, to prevent any oils bleeding through and staining a paint finish.

Anti-Humidity Paint is an absorbent and decorative coating consisting of a flat oil paint with finely granulated cork impregnated in it. It is available in pastel tints and can be simply applied to any good plaster or cement/sand renderings on ceiling or wall surfaces. One coat is sufficient over an efficient primer, but the compound must be liberally applied without much brushing, with the result that it has low covering power to the gallon. One particular variety of anti-humidity paint – Palorit (Quickset Water Sealers Ltd.) – sets hard enough to be scrubbed down with soap and water, and in addition, withstands temperatures up to 800°F.; it is therefore itself a fire-resisting finish of high quality.

Anti-Rust Paint (see under Aluminium Paint and Bitumen-base Paint).

Bitumen-base Paint has very high rust-preventing properties and is consequently used for tanks, and any metal work exposed to severe damp. A drawback to its use, however, is that it is not practicable to over-paint at any time in white or pastel colours, because of the tendency for it to bleed through and stain the finish. In cases where light colour finishes are required aluminium paint is the best form of sealer.

Cement-base Paints and colour washes, suitable for applying by brush or spray to ceiling and wall surfaces, are available in a fairly wide range of pale and medium-strength colours. They are mostly produced by diluting specially prepared cement-paint liquid-colour with water, and adding it to white cement to a suitable consistency for application by brush or spray. Application should be to an unpainted surface, free from lime-wash, distemper or other loose matter, and it must be well damped down before application, and again 24 hours after application. The same applies to a second coat.

Cement Enamel Finish (see also under *Cold glaze*). Sometimes referred to as Cement Glaze, it is a pure white cement (tinted when necessary), gauged with a special liquid which causes it to dry with a natural hard glaze. The application, being a special process, cannot be left to the general contractor, but is carried through by manufacturers' own specialists. It can be applied in situ direct to a Portland-cement/sand-rendered wall, shuttered concrete, or direct to flush-pointed brickwork. The cost can be roughly stated as half that of tiling or glazed bricks. In addition to a wide range of slightly mottled colours, it can also be produced in two-colour effects where the two colours are each visible, as in a terrazzo finish, or can be combined to give a 'shot' effect. Writing or scribbling on the spotted or stippled surface is claimed to be impossible.

Chlorinated-rubber Paint has very good acid-resisting properties, and is suitable for parts of laboratories, factories and other buildings where acid fumes are likely.

Cold Glaze is a name given to an extremely hard-wearing, non-porous decorative finish, which can be applied direct to concrete, to cement-and-sand renderings, and to brickwork. It forms a seamless glaze, with a mottled or plain stippled surface, in almost any colour. It is particularly well suited to large kitchens of hotels, restaurants, hospitals and canteens, and to entrance halls, staircases and corridors in public buildings, where a permanent scheme of decoration is required. It is immune against acids and alkali-concentrated solutions, and unaffected by heat up to 300°F. It would be equally well suited to kitchens and many parts of domestic buildings but for the fact that the manufacturers are insistent that all work must be carried out by their own specialists. This considerably limits the application of an otherwise most efficient finish, since it ceases to be an economic proposition when a team of specialist fixers have to travel a considerable distance to a job in which only a small area has to be treated.

Liquid Lino Floor-paint is a special preparation for application to linoleum flooring. It forms a hard, wear-resisting finish in a full range of remarkably good intense colours. When applied to stone and cement floors, which must be over six months old, this finish makes them easier to clean.

Metal-based Paints. Various metal paints are available consisting of finely ground bronze-metal powders of various shades of gold, copper and silver, and these are mixed with a special varnish medium which dries in normal time of 6–8 hours. Aluminium paste is also used instead of powder.

Generally speaking, ready-made-up metal paints are slightly less bright than when the powder is freshly mixed at the time it is required.

Plastic Paints. There are a number of efficient paints on the market sufficiently bodied to form a solid finish over all types of surface with one coat. Surface porosity must first be stopped by a suitable sealer. The surface produced is easily manipulated and a great variety of textural effects can be produced. Amongst the oldest and best-known brands are Marb-l-cote and Stic. B. Paint. Ordinary oil paint cannot be applied on top of these preparations.

Stone-base Paint is made from finely ground stone incorporated with a special emulsion, and has a high degree of resistance to damp, weather and fire. It is suitable for application by brush or spray to a great variety of surfaces, including concrete, stucco, brick, plaster, asbestos cement, building boards and painted and distempered surfaces. A very good colour-range is available and a hard and durable finish obtained, which in some cases will withstand heat up to 800°F.

11. WOOD VENEERS

Although wood veneer is used to a vast extent in all kinds of interior work, it is surprising that so few architects and designers will go to the trouble of selecting and specifying the more distinctive types. The bulk of all veneered work to-day is in mahogany, walnut or oak, and yet there are stocks of the most beautiful veneers lying in larger suppliers' warehouses which are rarely, if ever, used.

In order to avoid as much trouble as possible, contractors, shopfitters and the like are inclined to exaggerate the difference in cost between the standard veneered boards and specially selected veneers which have to be specially mounted on a suitable backing. Owing to the ease with which the standard material can be specified, obtained and used the demand for rarer veneers – each with individual limitations – has been so reduced that costs have increased much less than have those of materials formerly in the lower price-range. Providing the designer accepts the extra trouble of choosing veneer and arranging joints to suit the size limitations of the material selected, the extra cost is not great. A recent check showed that the average cost of veneer in a standard veneered board would be between sixpence and a shilling per square foot, whereas superb specimens of a large range of rarer woods can be bought at an average price of 1s. 6d. per square foot. Where comparatively small areas are required and these play a prominent part in the scheme, the *extra* cost of superlative material over the commonest wood, which is devoid of any real character, is negligible. What the extra 6d. per square foot gives the client is certainly better value than the 5s. which he has to spend in any case on a blockboard or laminated board backing.

'*Rollywood*' is the trade name of a relatively new material of Swedish origin (marketed by A. Sanderson & Son) which, although a genuine veneer product, can be applied to most flat or curved surfaces as simply as wall-paper, by means of a latex-type mastic. It consists of narrow parallel strips of natural wood woven together at intervals by means of thread. An outstanding advantage is that it can be obtained by the foot-run up to 60 ft. long in widths of 4 ft. and sometimes 8 ft. Five varieties are available – mahogany, zebra, walnut, obechi and a two-tone effect of alternate light and dark strips. Price 2s.–3s. per square foot.

12. WALL-PAPER

Although this finish has been in common use in domestic work for over two centuries, it has comparatively recently enjoyed a 'renaissance' which has come about as a result of a combination of circumstances. The most important of these is the growing tendency towards a freer treatment of interior design in which bolder effects are aimed at. To-day the majority of the younger generation at any rate are no longer shocked at the thought of applying a patterned and possibly strong-coloured wall-paper to one wall of a room only, and finishing the other three walls in a quiet and restful plain-coloured distemper.

If any logical defence for this practice is needed for elderly relatives who are inclined to ask 'when are the other walls going to be finished?' a reasonable explanation might be that after a quarter of a century of beige and off-white interiors, and years of all kinds of other restrictions, a little really strong colour acts as a most refreshing tonic, but to have all four walls of a room the same intense colour would be overpowering, and in every way unsatisfactory. There is no doubt that, in the hands of a good contemporary designer, few materials can compete with wall-paper for producing a lightning transformation in interiors, whether old or new, at extremely low cost.

The cost of wall-paper varies from about 4s. 6d. to over 35s. per piece, which is 11½ yards long and 21 inches wide when trimmed. A useful rough calculation which will serve as a guide to the quantity required, is that in a room of average height – say 8 ft. 6 in. to 9 ft. – one piece will safely cover four 21-in. widths. The cost of hanging can be roughly reckoned at 25s. per piece in the London area, but possibly a little less in other parts of the country.

There are literally thousands of patterns to choose from, but still very few that are likely to suit the contemporary designer. A vast number can best be summed up as 'off-porridge' in both texture and colour. Another large group consists of variations on the Edwardian conception of wall-paper – small-scale floral effects with endless repetition of roses, lovers' knots, trellis and foliage, each pattern offered in three or four shades – pale pink, pale blue, pale green and beige or buff.

Wall-paper manufacturers, with one or two exceptions, seem to show great reluctance or timidity in following the lead of interior designers, and considering the fact that the cost of cutting a new pattern-roller is a great deal less than the making of moulds, for instance, in other industries, one is inclined to feel they are not, on the whole, playing as prominent a part as might be expected in the field of contemporary interior design. There are nevertheless a few notable exceptions. As elsewhere, modern research is constantly discovering new technical tricks, and new processes occasionally produce interesting results.

The ease and rapidity with which striking effects can be achieved by means of wall-paper have resulted in its being much used in shop window backgrounds, exhibition stands and display of all kinds. It has also been invaluable to interior designers during the difficult years of restriction, when little or nothing could be spent on interior alterations and decoration. Where it is out of the question to employ natural wood finishes on account of cost, some of the wood-veneer papers provide a tolerably convincing substitute on wall surfaces, flush doors, counter fronts, and so on, and, providing they are not expected to stand undue wear, serve the purpose very well for a few years.

One point in connection with the use of wall-paper which it may be helpful to stress here, is that it is almost entirely printed in colour which has a china-clay base, with the result that it is by no means fast and will not stand up to rubbing with a damp cloth. This is not so apparent with pale colours but dark colours will smear very easily and great care must be exercised, when hanging, not to get any paste or damp on the face of the paper.

13. VENETIAN AND OTHER BLINDS

The popularity of the Venetian blind seems steadily to have increased since its re-birth in light metal or plastic form, and its universal adoption in the United

States, Canada, and in fact all parts of the world which are blessed with more sunshine than the British Isles.

There is no doubt that the precise line-texture lends itself admirably to the contemporary idiom, and the installation of Venetian blinds can contribute largely towards producing an up-to-date appearance in the conversion or re-modelling of old premises. They are manufactured on mass-production lines, with the result that the cost of the average installation is not heavy – roughly in the region of 5*s.* per square foot of their total area. Laths can be supplied in quite a large range of standard colours and ladder-tapes are also available in a selection of colours.

Apart from their domestic uses, which are to provide infinitely adjustable light, draught-free ventilation, and privacy, Venetian blinds are extensively applied in business offices, administrative suites, shops, department stores, etc. Their general appearance is attractive enough for them frequently to be seen as backgrounds for window displays, for screening, and for lightweight partitions temporarily subdividing floor space.

Limitations of Venetian blinds are roughly as follows: width, up to 10 ft.; drop, 10 ft.; tapes are spaced approximately 2 ft.–10 in. apart and the outer-most tapes are $6\frac{3}{4}$ in. from the ends of the laths.

Accordo Blinds. These are pleated fabric blinds which are available in a number of pale tints, and in any width up to 20 ft. A vertical Monel metal guide rod passes through the pleated fabric at either end to prevent flapping owing to wind-pressure when the window is open. Unique features of these blinds are that they can be adjusted from either the top or the bottom with equal ease, and they can also be fitted to horizontal laylights and north-light roofs. Accordo blinds are being installed in many schools throughout the country and are equally applicable to any windows of offices, hospitals, or buildings in which shading from bright sunlight is necessary. A dark blind is also available for laboratories. The price of these blinds is in the region of 4*s.* per sq. ft.

14. NATURAL HIDE

The use of natural hide need not be confined to the upholstery of chairs and settees, neither is it necessarily a very expensive finish. It can, in fact, be quite the reverse, but a few simple points need to be understood before it can be economically applied, and one of the factors which has a direct influence on this is the size and shape of the unit used. The economical way is to buy whole skins, and to contrive a unit which fits economically into the shape of the whole skin with as little waste as possible. Whole skins vary a good deal in size, but coming as they do off animals of similar form, the shape varies very little – every skin having a leg at each corner, as it were, and a neck at one end.

A certain amount of ingenuity and intelligence is therefore necessary when

EQUIPMENT. 171. *Flexible aluminium venetian blinds (J. Avery and Co. Ltd.) in the main exhibition room of the headquarters of the British Rayon and Synthetic Fibres Federation, Piccadilly, London. The radiator screens are of woven cane. (Designer: R. D. Russell.) 172. Standard school cloakroom equipment in stove-enamelled malleable cast iron. (A. J. Binns Ltd.)*

171

172

173

174

175

ELECTRICAL FITTINGS. 173. *A skirting socket combining three plugs neatly into one component and so avoiding the usual unsightly collection of adaptors; all the plugs are fused. (New Day Electrical Accessories Ltd.)* 174. *A plug with points in the socket instead of the usual arrangement of pins on the plug is a useful and safe device for portable apparatus; the illustration shows the Lundberg 2 amp. type. (Simplex Electric Co.)* 175. *A 13 amp. plug adaptor with rectangular pins has a fused adaptor to prevent overloading; two fused adaptors can be used plus a normal plug; the illustration shows the Ediswan Clix model. (Edison Swan Electric Co.)*

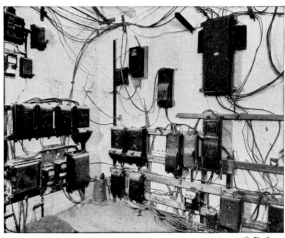

176 Before

176a After

176 *(before) and* 176a *(after). Comparative pictures showing, (*176*), a common state of affairs in a wiring installation near the fuse boxes and, (*176a*), how the installation could look if tidied up by wiring on the vertical rising-main system with wires enclosed in conduits and fuse boxes united into two large units. (General Electric Co. Ltd).*

deciding to use natural hide in interior work, and if exacting demands are made – such as to have panels seven or eight feet long – the cost may appear prohibitive simply because only one panel could probably be cut out of each skin. Providing, therefore, that the job is designed to fit the animal, and waste is avoided, six to seven pounds, which is the cost of a skin of average size, cannot be considered excessive in view of the yield of thirty to thirty-five square feet of hide. A considerable range of standard colours is available, and is supplied by any of the best known merchants; the quality does not vary to any appreciable extent.

There is little variety in the technique of applying hide to the requirements of interior work, and most examples fall into one of two or three well-tried methods. All depend on a reliable backing, blockboard, plywood, or substitute. The hide is stretched, turned over the ends, and tacked at the back. A quilted effect can be produced by slightly padding the face with a layer of soft, easily-compressed material, such as wadding, and buttoning at regular-spaced points. If the buttons are covered in hide or fabric of a contrasting colour, a more decorative effect is produced. Directional emphasis, either vertical or horizontal, can be produced by the same layer of padding, but by stitching or tacking in parallel lines. Joints can either be sewn neatly, as with other fabrics, or further emphasis can be given to the join by fixing a piping which can be in a different colour if required. This sort of treatment is most appropriately used as a finish to fairly small areas, such as the fronts of cocktail and snackbar counters, where it is an advantage to have something tough and yet fairly soft and comfortable-looking.

Synthetic Hide
This is marketed under a number of different trade names, such as Plastahide, and in a similar colour range to the natural hides. Its only advantage over the natural product is that it is obtainable by the yard in a standard width of 36 in., which eliminates the waste which is liable to occur in the natural product. It is made in a variety of textures – in imitation of natural hides and also in a number of mechanically-embossed textures. The cost is in the region of 8s. per yard, 36-in. wide, and the method of application is by sewing in the same way as leather, or by special adhesives recommended by the manufacturers.

15. COLOUR SYSTEMS AND COLOUR SCHEMES
Much is heard from time to time about colour systems of one kind or another, and many of the larger paint manufacturing firms have departments full of colour theorists who have built up an elaborate science from a few simple facts, augmented and complicated by psychological theories. Effects of light on colour, and one colour on another, are infinitely subtle, and cannot be reduced to mathematical formulae and applied automatically to interiors of every description. Such colour systems may be wholly satisfactory when applied to

the multiplicity of individual parts of interiors such as large industrial plants and factories. Any building, however, in which the interior is of real consequence should have the benefit of the individuality and experience of an interior specialist, if the architect lacks the confidence, or has insufficient time to devote to colour finishes.

However well a colour scheme may suit the interior for which it was devised, it could not necessarily be applied to any other room and be expected to give an equally satisfactory result, unless the two interiors were identical in lighting, aspect, and scale. Undoubtedly these formulated colour schemes are a considerable improvement on the past, when the bulk of the architectural profession seemed to be opposed to the use of colour and rarely ventured beyond cream and brown or green.

16. METAL FINISHES

Metals play an important part in interior work – more in the form of functional components than in a purely decorative form. Sheet metals are used for cladding – or pressed into special components, such as window frames, door frames, stair treads, cover strips and mouldings of many kinds. Channels and an infinite variety of intricate sections are extruded for fixing glazing, or other sheet materials. Metals are also used in spinnings, deep drawn pressings and castings.

Owing to the necessity for steel and brass in the armament field, aluminium has had to play by far the largest part in supplying the needs of the interior designer, and great progress has been made in recent years both in technical development towards greater strength, and also in ingenuity in design with the object of economy in material. Aluminium can be worked by most of the processes normally applied in metal work – castings, extruding, drawing, sheet panel beating, bending, spinning, deep drawing and pressing, stretch forming, stamping, machining, welding, brazing and soldering, riveting and bolting. Because of its high resistance to atmospheric influences aluminium is often used with nothing more than its normal manufactured finish, but in more prominent positions and in better-class work a variety of decorative finishes can be applied. Mechanical finishes consist of polishing, burnishing and satin finish, and each produces a characteristic appearance.

Anodizing
This is an electro-chemical process whereby the natural oxide film of the aluminium is thickened by making it the anode in a cell through which a current is passed. The thick oxide film thus produced is hard and strongly adherent, being integral with the metal, but its most important property is its outstanding resistance to chemical attack. The anodized surface can take dyes in a wide range of colours which are resistant to light and heat; also, by special treatment, designs and photographs can be reproduced on the metal.

208

Painting

As with most metals, the surface of aluminium should generally be treated before painting, to secure the maximum adhesion. Components of reasonable size are dipped, but where their shape or size makes this impossible, they may be treated with brushing preparations, subsequently removed by swilling with water. Priming paints are now available, known as 'wash primers', which give maximum adhesion without pre-treatment. Paints and lacquers are brushed, sprayed, or rolled onto the treated surface, and providing an efficient primer has been used, any good paint or enamel compatible with the primer may be used for the finishing coats in accordance with decorative requirements. If the surface should become scratched, corrosion very rarely spreads under the paint, as the natural oxide film usually affords adequate protection. Aluminium, therefore, requires re-painting less frequently than steel.

Stove Enamel Finish

This is applicable to all kinds of fabricated metalwork in iron, steel and aluminium. Aluminium requires priming with a special preparation before it can be treated.

This extremely hard and durable finish is produced by coating the article with a special synthetic low-bake enamel, and 'stoving' it in an oven at a temperature of about 250°F.

For this reason application of the process is limited by the size of the oven. The average enclosed 'Boxoven' will take anything up to $6 \times 4 \times 3$ ft.

A full range of colour is possible in this finish, and although at one time mainly 'utility' colours – grey, buff and cream – were used, it is now frequently seen as a finish for spun aluminium lighting fittings in bright primary colours.

Even local authorities are beginning to be more colour-conscious, and lighting fittings and other metal components in schools and public buildings, which a few years ago would have been chromium-plated, are now being finished in stove enamel.

Among the more recent additions to this field, and worthy of mention, is the complete school cloakroom equipment which has been thoroughly well worked out in as straightforward and economical a way as possible, by A. J. Binns Ltd., in stove-enamelled malleable cast iron (Fig. 172, p. 205).

17. MISCELLANEOUS FITTINGS

The whole field of 'Architectural Metalwork', as it was frequently termed until the Plastic Industry began to compete, has shown – and still unfortunately shows – little trace of progress throughout the last thirty or forty years.

Most of its output was badly designed, crudely made and can hardly be described as finished in any technical sense.

It is admittedly not easy to make functional components of this nature pleasing in form, since form is often so precisely dictated by requirements as to leave little opportunity for the designer. We do however expect to find as many kinks and sharp corners as possible smoothed off, and a reasonably 'easy-to-clean' finish, whereas in many examples manufacturers have deliberately introduced kinks and effects in a misguided attempt at design, and it is at these points that corrosion invariably starts.

In spite of this lamentable situation a few good straightforward fittings can be found for most purposes, and out of a very large range of mediocre examples, a few can even be procured which, although anything up to fifteen years old, might be said still to be equally suitable in contemporary design as they were when first produced. Nevertheless the poor design of standard fastenings and handles for doors and windows is a matter which deserves the immediate and serious attention of bodies like the Council of Industrial Design and the Design and Industries Association.

The younger industries, unencumbered by past traditions, occasionally give a glimpse of what can be achieved where there is the will to improve design. In the modern motor car, the refrigerator, the electric iron and numerous examples of new equipment, we often see beautifully sculptured shapes for handles which are as attractive to hold as they are to look at.

Although it may be encroaching on matters dealt with in the next section,* mention should perhaps be made of a group of electrical components that has recently become available, which are a pleasant relief from the bulky and clumsy types almost invariably installed hitherto. In addition to being pleasant in appearance, and available in ivory as well as the inevitable brown bakelite, one of the assemblies fulfils a long existing requirement. Although for many years, almost every living-room, bed-sitting-room and often bedroom has required, in addition to a heating point, a lighting point for a floor standard or reading lamp, and a point for a radio, yet the electrical industry as a whole has done little or nothing about it. The result can be seen in almost any house – a motley and unsightly collection of adaptors has been fitted to supply lights and radio, while the heating point forms a separate obstruction by the side, or on the opposite side of the fire-place. The 'New Day' fireside triple socket combines all these neatly into one component. Another equally well-designed component is a micro-gap tumbler double switch plate which is only fractionally larger than the single switch plate. There is also a single switch plate which is $3\frac{1}{4} \times 1\frac{3}{8}$ in. wide, for application to narrow door architraves.

Author's Note. – I gratefully acknowledge the ready assistance given me in the preparation of this section by C. F. Anderson & Son Ltd., Wallboards and Plastics Department (on wall-boards); by David Esdaile & Co. Ltd. (on fibrous plaster); by Goodlass Wall & Co. Ltd. (on paints); and by Jaconello Ltd. (on floors and flooring materials). K.C.

* See also p. 213.—Ed.

BIBLIOGRAPHY

CEMENT FINISHES
Painting Asbestos Cement. (B.R.S. Digest No. 38, January, 1952. H.M.S.O.)

FLOORS
Floor Finishes. F. C. Harper. (Journal of the R.I.B.A., March, 1951.)
Top Dressing. H. McG. Dunnett. (Architectural Review, February, 1953.)

GLASS
Glass in Architecture and Decoration. Raymond McGrath and A. C. Frost. (Architectural Press, 1937. Out of print.)
Glass in Modern Buildings. M. L. Anderson. (Journal of the R.I.B.A., 1933.)
New Ways of Building. Eric de Maré, editor. (Architectural Press, 1951.)

METAL FINISHES
Anodic Oxidation of Aluminium and its Alloys. (Information Bulletin No. 14, Aluminium Development Association.)
Surface Finishing of Aluminium and its Alloys. (Information Bulletin No. 13, Aluminium Development Association.)

PAINTS AND ALLIED FINISHES
Distempers on Walls and Ceilings. (B.R.S. Digest No. 22, September, 1950. H.M.S.O.)
Emulsion Paints. (B.R.S. Digest No. 50, January, 1953. H.M.S.O.)
Outlines of Paint Technology. Noel Heaton. (Charles Griffin & Co. Ltd. London, 1947.)
Painting and Decorating. D. W. Marshall. (Illustrated Carpenter and Builder, 1951.)
Painting and Decoration. A. E. Hurst. (Charles Griffin & Co. Ltd. London, 1949.)
Painting, Staining and Varnishing Wood and Treatment with Preservatives. (British Standards Institution. General Series Codes 2.41.)
Painting Woodwork. (B.R.S. Digest No. 30, May, 1951. H.M.S.O.)

TILES
Tiling (Floor and Wall) and Paving. F. W. M. Eglinton. (Crosby Lockwood, London, 1939.)
Wall and Floor Tiling. Cyril Carter and H. R. Hidden. (Caxton Publishing Co., London.)

WALL AND CEILING BOARDS
Wall Board Development in Britain. (Booklet published by C. F. Anderson & Sons., Harris Wharf, Graham Street, N.1.)

WALL PAPER
Specification for Wall Paper. (Published by Wall Paper Manufacturers Ltd. Manchester and London, 1953.)

WOOD VENEERS
Decorative Wood Veneers. J. L. Robertson. (Journal of the R.I.B.A., October, 1953.)

ADDENDA   *Philip Scholberg*

1. RING MAINS

From the point of view of housing some of the most interesting post-war developments are the changes now allowed in wiring systems, which may save considerable amounts of cable and installation costs. In the pre-war years it was always the rule that power sockets had to be fed independently with separate circuits running back to a main fuse box, nor was it permissible for 5- and 15-amp. sockets to be fed from the same fuse. Under the revised regulations it is now possible to have a 30-amp. main switch, fused on the live side only, and serving all the sockets in the house via a ring main. Fig. 177 shows the compactness and simplicity of the new system, and it is immediately obvious that there should be a considerable saving in the amount of cable required, while the size need not be increased beyond the 7/.029 normally needed to

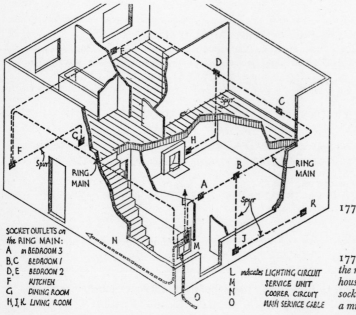

SOCKET OUTLETS *on*
the RING MAIN:
A *in* BEDROOM 3
B, C BEDROOM 1
D, E BEDROOM 2
F KITCHEN
G DINING ROOM
H, I, K LIVING ROOM

L *indicates* LIGHTING CIRCUIT
M SERVICE UNIT
N COOKER CIRCUIT
O MAIN SERVICE CABLE

177

177. *Diagram showing how the ring main runs round the house to feed one or more sockets in each room, using a minimum of cable.*

212

supply a single 15-amp. socket. At first glance it may seem that this is merely giving permission to overload the circuit, but in actual practice this is not at all likely to occur, as domestic wiring circuits have a high diversity factor, the sockets seldom being used to their full capacity at the same time, so that the cable size may be kept low. As the circuit is fed from both ends a total loading of 30 amps., or nearly 7 kilowatts, is below the rating of the normal 15-amp. cable.

So far as the sockets themselves are concerned only a single type is used to the appropriate BSS (1363) which specifies a rectangular shape for the plug pins and sockets, with the further proviso that the plugs must be fitted with a cartridge fuse. The sockets are rated at 13 amps., this figure having been chosen because with the now almost standardized voltage of 230 it will give a capacity of 3 kilowatts. The cartridge fuse in the plug must be of the size appropriate for the appliance being used, whether it be a 3-kilowatt fire or a 25-watt reading lamp. While it may seem at first glance a retrograde step to add a further standard to those already existing, it is difficult to see how it could have been avoided, and it is reasonable to assume that the round pin 5- and 15-amp. sockets will ultimately disappear. It should be added that cookers, which may have a total loading of six or seven kilowatts, should not be connected to the ring main, but must have a separate circuit.

2. SWITCHES, CONTROLS AND SOCKETS

In the design of switches there have been few major developments, but the slow make and break types are now far more widely used. They have the advantage that they are quite silent in operation and are thus particularly suitable for use in hospitals or nurseries, and they are also simpler to produce. It should be emphasized, however, that they are only suitable for use with alternating current supplies. Simmerstat controls, first used for the ovens or hot plates of electric cookers, give an infinite variation between off and full on, and are now produced as controls for wall sockets so that the heat from an electric fire may be accurately controlled. Other special-purpose sockets and switches include the types arranged to switch on or off when a door or cupboard is opened or closed, and a more recent development is a multi-outlet socket with a small transformer to provide the different voltages and accept the varying plugs fitted to British, American or Continental electric razors. This seems a useful fitting for hotels, and is quite cheap.

3. WIRING

Methods of wiring have also undergone development. Conduit remains much as before, but at least one firm is producing plastic conduit, junctions and outlet boxes, the conduit being flexible enough to be easily bent by hand and also very smooth internally so that the cables may be easily drawn in.

For cable coverings rubber still remains the standard material, but P.V.C. is widely used, as well as other plastics, having the advantage that the covering is thinner and that more wires can therefore be run in the same size of conduit. Fire-resisting coverings are also produced by most members of the Cable Makers' Association, while aluminium is used for sheathing as an alternative to lead. It has the advantage of added stiffness, so that supports for cables need not be so closely spaced.

For electrical distribution in the larger building it is also becoming common practice to arrange a rising main of copper rods (three-phase and neutral) in a vertical duct with the necessary distribution boards at each floor. With this system it becomes much easier to balance the total load across phases.

4. COMMUNICATION SYSTEMS

The internal telephone systems in the larger buildings are still much the same, but there is a growing tendency, particularly in factories, to arrange a loud-speaker system for the popular 'Music-While-You-Work' broadcasts, and this can be extended for making general announcements, for finding staff, and also for marking the end of the shift or the start of a tea break. It is possible for the regular time-keeping announcements or calls to be made automatically with a time clock.

5. HAND DRIERS, INCINERATORS, INSECT EXTERMINATORS

A number of manufacturers are now producing the hand driers, incinerators and other units which are now demanded for office and factory cloakrooms. Electric hand driers contain a fan and a heating element for the air, and are an efficient alternative to the fabric or paper towels, the cost of which tends to become high. Electric- or gas-operated automatic incinerators for disposal of women's sanitary towels are now also regarded as essential in any office or factory, and also in hotels and restaurants. For the kitchens of the latter it is now quite usual to provide one of the small units which distribute D.D.T. or some similar insect exterminator in aerosol form. These small particles float in the air and there is no need for the dusting of powder or spraying of liquids.

6. SMALL AIR-CONDITIONING UNITS

Heating systems are dealt with elsewhere, but small air-conditioning units now in production should be mentioned here. These normally fit into the space beneath a window, and have a suction fan, humidifier control, and a refrigerating unit. (Figs. 81, 82, page 96.) The air is drawn in through a filter, dehumidified and cooled and circulated in the room, and there is also an adjustment which allows a proportion of the air already in the room to be re-circulated. Some units are also equipped with electric heaters for use in cold weather when

SCREEN. 178. *The new booking office screen at Paddington Station, London, may provide ideas for the designing of partitioning. The panels between the ticket windows are of cellular plastic sheeting veneered with sapele mahogany; the dado below the mahogany counter is of 1 in. faience tiles facing 3 in. clinker blocks; the area above the ticket windows is panelled with 6 ft. sheets of broad-reeded glass fixed to patent glazing bars; the strip below the glazing is of aluminium-faced plywood between an abura wood frame; the ceiling is of suspended boarding; and the floor is of terrazzo with coved skirting. (Architects: W. R. Headley, T. P. Wurr and Margaret Aitken of the Architect's office of British Railways, Western Region.)*

179

PARTITIONS. 179. *A standard type of office partitioning of steel and glass; the steel posts are made in two halves bolted together to hold the panelling which is of steel sheet filled with insulating material; the glazing can start at any height; doors are hung in sub-frames fixed to*

180

the steel posts. (Sankey Sheldon Ltd.; see also fig. 188, p. 220.) 180. Plastic panels fixed with extruded members and special sections for door frames and glazing. The panels are hollow and can be filled with insulation. The faces can be veneered or painted. Also the patterned plastic finishes can be used. (Holoplast Ltd.; see also fig. 190, p. 220.) 181. A specially designed partition for a factory in which the height of 25 ft. made it necessary to produce built-up spars partly exposed and running the full height. (Compactom Ltd.)

181

the cooling unit is not needed. It is worth mentioning that if a cooling system is required in any public building it is advisable to install fluorescent rather than tungsten lamps, as the latter, with the elaborate lighting systems now popular, give out a considerable amount of heat.

7. LIFT GEAR

Changes in lift gear include revised systems of push-button control coupled with the use of automatic doors. Lifts can now be set to stop at a series of floors, when the doors will open and close automatically, the lift finally returning to the ground or any other selected floor. The doors are normally timed to remain open for a specified time, ten or fifteen seconds, but they have safety devices in the closing edges so that if a passenger should be in the way the door re-opens at once. It is also possible to arrange overriding controls so that 'higher executives' can summon a lift wherever it may be, full or not. Refinements such as these are perhaps not essential but are mentioned to show that almost anything is possible if there should be a demand for it.

8. KITCHEN EQUIPMENT

Among the kitchen equipment are the cabinets of standard dimensions, produced by a number of different firms. With the introduction of comparatively cheap electric washing machines extra space beneath draining boards or table tops is often required, and since these machines are within the purchasing power of the lower income groups it is sometimes possible for the copper to be omitted from local authority housing. The service hatch, in which tradesmen can safely leave goods when the housewife is out, was occasionally used before the war, but now, although not standard practice, is very widely used. The same may be said of externally filled coal bunkers, which, though more difficult to arrange, are desirable, less from the point of view of deliveries when the house or flat is empty, than for the prevention of coal dust being trodden through the house.

9. TELEVISION AERIALS

However unsightly they may be, it is not always possible to avoid the use of multi-element externally mounted television aerials, for the users of the sets quite naturally demand that reception should be as good as is reasonably possible in the area concerned. In districts near the transmitting station, and where interference from external sources is small, it may be possible to use an indoor aerial fitted in the same room as the receiver, or integral with it, but the picture may be affected by people moving about in the room, or by other indoor aerials in the same building. Moreover these aerials are, as a rule, unsuitable for use in steel-framed buildings.

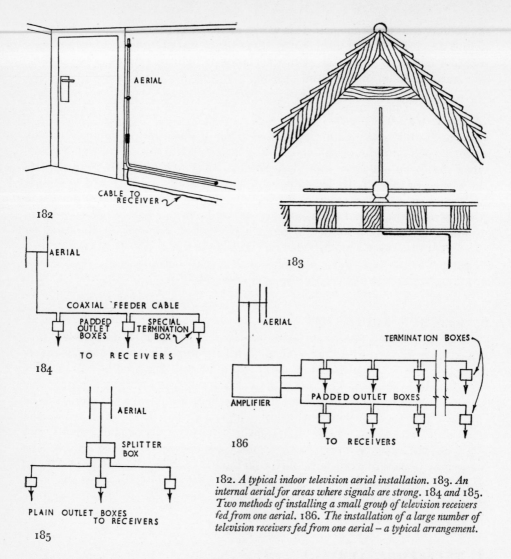

AERIAL

CABLE TO RECEIVER

182

AERIAL

COAXIAL FEEDER CABLE

PADDED OUTLET BOXES

SPECIAL TERMINATION BOX

TO RECEIVERS

184

183

AERIAL

SPLITTER BOX

PLAIN OUTLET BOXES
TO RECEIVERS

185

AERIAL

AMPLIFIER

TERMINATION BOXES

PADDED OUTLET BOXES

TO RECEIVERS

186

182. *A typical indoor television aerial installation.* 183. *An internal aerial for areas where signals are strong.* 184 *and* 185. *Two methods of installing a small group of television receivers fed from one aerial.* 186. *The installation of a large number of television receivers fed from one aerial – a typical arrangement.*

Where signals can be classified as strong, and where external interference remains moderate, then an aerial in the roof space will often be adequate, but it is, unfortunately, impossible to give any hard and fast rules, and each installation must depend on local conditions. In strong signal areas it is possible to arrange that a number of receivers are fed from a single aerial, generally with an amplifier. This is an excellent system for closely grouped housing estates, and is probably the only neat and practicable method for flat blocks. A complete installation will usually cost less per point than individual aerials.

For all television aerial problems advice can be obtained from the Radio and

Electronic Component Manufacturers Federation, 22 Surrey Street, London, W.C.2, or the British Radio Equipment Manufacturers Association, 59 Russell Square, London, W.C.1.

10. FIRE PRECAUTIONS

In the items of equipment used for fire protection – sprinklers, extinguishers, hoses and so on – there has been no significant change, but, as a result of war-time experiences, the general approach to problems of fire risk has altered a great deal. The term 'fire load' is used to indicate the amount of heat which may be liberated by the building and its contents, and is thus also a measure of the temperature which may be reached during a fire. In the estimating of risks more attention is also being paid to the form in which a material is used. For example, timber beams whose volume will be considerable in relation to their surface area will burn comparatively slowly, whereas lightly framed and panelled furniture might be classified as kindling, being rapidly combustible.

As a result of sundry unfortunate experiences with wall-facing materials in sheet form, more attention is being paid to the rate of flame spread of different forms of surface finish. The Fire Research Testing Station at Elstree has evolved a standard test and a grading system, and nearly all the makers of sheet materials submit their products for test and grading. A number of chemical products are now also made which, when brushed or pressure-applied to porous materials, will reduce the rate of flame spread. The majority of the manufac-turers of paint and other purely surface decorating materials will also supply flame-spread figures if required.

11. PARTITIONS

In the design of both permanent and movable partitions there have been con-siderable changes. Plastering is a skilled trade and time must be wasted while the various coats dry, and manufacturers have concentrated mainly on parti-tions which can be quickly erected by semi-skilled labour and which will need, at most, a skim coat only. Building boards may be made from wood chips, plastics, plywood, plaster or compressed straw, and in panels of room-height, usually with a width of 4 ft. Many of these sheet materials are assembled into panels at the factory, either on a timber framing or on a light-weight core which may be of many different materials from cork slab to a cellular structure of heavy cardboard.

Other types of partition have been evolved which may be classified as semi-permanent in that they can be used in office buildings and moved without any difficulty if the internal layout has to be revised. Most of these systems are based on a series of metal uprights spaced at panel width, with channels at floor and ceiling, so that when a partition has to be moved only a minimum of making

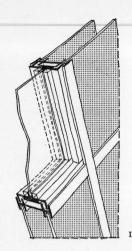

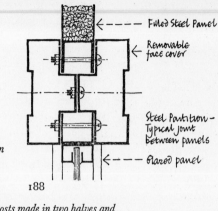

187. *'Gypstele' partition in a steel frame with an infilling of gypsum plaster panels. (Gyproc Products.)* 188. *Office partitioning with steel posts made in two halves and bolted together to hold the panelling. (Sankey Sheldon.)*

187

188

good is needed. Doors and glazed panels can be provided wherever they are needed, and the necessary uprights are produced in different sections to provide tee or angle junctions between the individual panels.

Panel materials vary considerably from a steel facing filled with gypsum plastic, cork, or some other insulating material, to light alloys and plastics, and there is at least one structural plastic panel, hollow and with internal ribs,

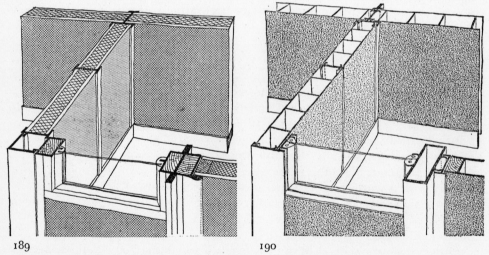

189

190

189. *A system in which the panels have a cork core which may be faced with hardboard, plastics or metal sheet. The panels are fixed with extruded light alloy channels at floor level, H sections at the vertical joints, with special extrusions for door or window frames and at corners. (Saunders Roe.)* 190. *Plastic panels fixed with extruded members and special sections for door frames and glazing. The panels are hollow and can be filled with insulation. The faces can be veneered or painted, and it is also possible to use the patterned plastic finishes. (Holoplast.)*

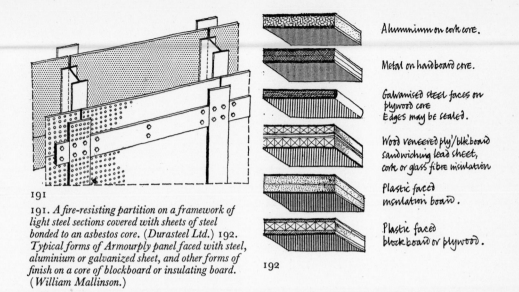

191. *A fire-resisting partition on a framework of light steel sections covered with sheets of steel bonded to an asbestos core. (Durasteel Ltd.)* 192. *Typical forms of Armourply panel faced with steel, aluminium or galvanized sheet, and other forms of finish on a core of blockboard or insulating board. (William Mallinson.)*

Aluminium on cork core.

Metal on hardboard core.

Galvanised steel faces on plywood core
Edges may be sealed.

Wood veneered ply/blk'board sandwiching lead sheet, cork or glass fibre insulation

Plastic faced insulation board.

Plastic faced blockboard or plywood.

which can be readily assembled and also, if necessary, faced with veneers or some other decorative finish during manufacture. These panels may be joined at their long edges by a wooden tongue pressed into the side groove, or by special extruded light alloy sections (see Fig. 190). Where the sections are visible they may be anodized and coloured to suit the scheme of decoration. With most of these systems of partitioning it is simple to run wiring systems for lighting, telephones and other services within the thickness of the panels or in the hollow uprights and to provide a neat and well-protected installation.

In the pre-war years various firms produced a system of partitioning with hollow glass blocks, giving good heat insulation and complete obscuration. Similar blocks are now made in transparent plastic, but the total height of any partition is limited to about half that permissible with glass, as the plastic blocks have a relatively low compressive strength.

Editor's Note. It is hardly possible to provide a Bibliography for this section. Much useful information about the subjects briefly discussed above can, however, be obtained in relevant trade periodicals, from manufacturers' technical handouts and in the appropriate British Standards Specifications (British Standards Institution, 2 Park Street, London, W.1).

In connection with fire protection, attention is drawn to an interesting discussion published in *The Architects' Journal*, March 25, 1954, on the combustibility of fibre insulation boards which centres round the question: 'Are fire resistance and insulation incompatible?' An official document on the subject is *Fire Hazard of Internal Linings*, a National Building Study Special Report No. 22.

GENERAL INDEX

Note: The italic numerals indicate pages on which half-tone illustrations appear.

227